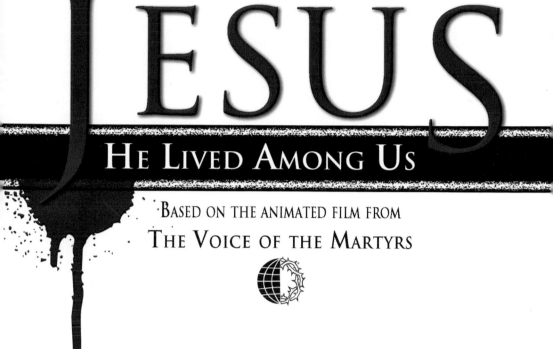

JESUS

HE LIVED AMONG US

BASED ON THE ANIMATED FILM FROM

THE VOICE OF THE MARTYRS

WRITTEN BY
R.F. PALAVICINI AND STEVE CLEARY

Published by Warner Press, Inc, Anderson, IN 46012
Warner Press and "WP" logo is a trademark of Warner Press, Inc.

ISBN: 978 1 59317-435-4

82985018156

Editors: Karen Rhodes, Robin Fogle
Cover by Curtis D. Corzine
Design and layout: Curtis D. Corzine, Kevin Spear and Christian Elden

*Dedicated to all those who are willing to risk life
and liberty to follow Christ.*

God sent His only Son, Jesus, to live as a man, walking among the people and teaching them about their Heavenly Father.

For centuries, people have been drawn to the story of Jesus. What is there about this man that would make people leave their homes and families to follow Him? What could possibly inspire them to love Jesus so much they would be willing to die for Him?

Jesus: He Lived Among Us is a retelling of the life of Christ, based on the animated film from The Voice of the Martyrs. This presentation of Christ's time on earth is a biblically based, dramatized narrative that takes the reader on an action-packed journey, depicting Jesus' life, including the persecution He and His followers experienced. These stories illustrate the profound effect His life had, both on His followers and on those who considered Him a threat.

While not your typical Bible storybook, *Jesus: He Lived Among Us* is a powerful learning tool for young people and adults as they discover Christ's relevance to their lives. Readers will be challenged to a deeper faith as they witness the sacrificial nature of those who follow the Christ who lived among us.

This book includes:

- Dramatized stories from the four Gospels
- Illustrations taken from the animated film to create a colorful depiction of the stories
- Scripture references for a more in-depth study
- Questions for further discussion

LIST OF STORIES

THE OLD PRISONER

He woke up to complete darkness.

He was tired, very tired. So tired that for an instant he hardly knew where he was. But the moment he tried to move and heard the rattling of chains, he remembered where he was and why.

The ship shuddered as it slammed against the wharf. By the distant yelling of the commander on deck, he knew they had reached their destination—the Isle of Patmos—the small, desolate island in the Aegean Sea, where the Roman Empire sent political prisoners and dangerous criminals…like the man in the darkness….

Except that he was not the sort most people would consider dangerous. He had not murdered or kidnapped anybody, never threatened anyone— had never even stolen anything. But he was a danger just the same.

The man was held prisoner because he was a follower of Jesus Christ—a man he had met as a young person, the One who had changed his life.

The sound of a creaking iron grate, followed by the thud of soldiers jumping down into his cell, brought the prisoner back to the present. Soldiers pulled him up by the iron shackles that had made his wrists nearly raw with the metal grating against his skin.

"Bring him up!" came the command from the deck.

The prisoner was thrown on the deck, landing at the commander's feet. The night was foggy, lit occasionally by flashes of lightning.

"Get up!"

No sooner had the commander reached down to grab the shackles than the prisoner clutched the commander's forearm instead, pulling himself to his feet.

He was weak and unsteady but the prisoner stood face-to-face with the commander, and then slowly made his way to the plank, chains dragging behind him as he crossed over onto the pier.

Soon they were making their way up steps carved into the rock. The prisoner, stumbling with the shackles around his ankles, didn't give in to the soldier's push.

"All's ready. Where's the prisoner?" a gruff voice rang out from the top of the steep incline where a shadowy figure stood, barely visible through the thick mist.

"Here he is, Titus," came the commander's reply as he pushed the prisoner forward. Step by step, the prisoner made his way to the top where the guard slowly came into view with his hand by his sword should the criminal give any trouble.

As the prisoner stepped out of the mist, the guard's nervousness changed into a look of utter shock. Finally he was standing before the dangerous criminal, the one the government called "a threat to Rome": a bruised and shivering, ninety-year-old man.

The old prisoner was thrown into a cave, hitting his head against a jagged wall and falling to the ground, where he lay moaning. Titus was clearly humiliated by his assignment to guard an old man.

"Have they gone mad in Rome?" He stepped into the cave, followed by the weary commander.

"Watch your words, Titus."

"Really. Why is he here?"

"*Dominus et Deus*," came the reply from the old prisoner as he did his best to sit up. Blood trickled from his forehead. "Lord and God. That is what the Emperor Domitian demands to be called."

"And?" Titus saw no meaning in this.

"There is only one Lord and God. The one I serve," came the reply.

Surprised, Titus turned to the commander who poured himself some wine. "They sent him here for that? Refusing to accept the emperor as God? Why didn't they just kill him?"

"They tried." The commander knew his explanation would sound unbelievable. "Except…he wouldn't die."

Titus burst into laughter, until he realized the commander remained straight-faced.

"What do you mean?"

"He's a Christian of some influence—encourages others to follow his so-called Savior. The man was warned, imprisoned and finally…boiled."

"Boiled?"

"That's right. He wouldn't die. Nothing happened."

For a moment, Titus thought the commander was joking with him. "Ah, nonsense!" he chuckled.

"Is it?" the commander slammed down his cup. "Then why do you think we're here? The old man wouldn't withdraw his loyalty to this Jesus Christ or stop talking about Him."

"How can I?" Weak as he was physically, the old prisoner's voice rang with strength. "Jesus gave His life for me, and for you as well. For everyone! He died on the cross to pay for our sins and bring us close to God. He rose from the dead and lives and has called us as His witnesses. His words bring life and joy. I can't withhold such wonderful truth from others!"

Titus could not understand it. Bruised, bleeding and in chains, the prisoner was actually smiling. It was upsetting and made him feel uneasy.

"Well, if you had, you could've saved yourself all this misery and lived your old age with some pleasure, isn't that right, commander?"

"You're a soldier," said the prisoner.

"That I am, old man! And a loyal one too!" retorted Titus proudly.

"Then you will understand what it means to defend something you believe in. I am honored to be here for Christ, in these chains. And what about you? Are you honored to be here for your empire?"

For a moment Titus was speechless and finding nothing to say, he simply got up and kicked a stool in anger while muttering, "Crazy old fool!"

The commander, on the other hand, was laughing so hard he nearly choked on the wine. When he finally composed himself, he asked, "But how do you know, old man? How are you so certain that this Jesus—that He is, what did you say—the Son of God?"

"Because I was there," came the reply.

And neither the commander nor Titus said a word. †

THE CHILD
Taken from Isaiah 7:14; Luke 1:26-30

"Therefore the Lord himself will give you a sign: The virgin will be with child and will give birth to a son, and will call him Immanuel." Isaiah 7:14

The night air had cooled and the commander brought his stool closer to the fire, wrapping his cape about his shoulders as Titus stoked the fire.

"There were signs from the very beginning," the old prisoner continued. "And a prophecy which said that a virgin would conceive a son."

"A virgin?" Titus wondered. "That's impossible!"

"Not with God," replied the prisoner. "With God, nothing is impossible." And as the guards listened, the old prisoner went on to tell the story he knew so well.

Nothing seemed out of the ordinary that night in the dark, whitewashed room in Galilee where a young woman lay sleeping. The soft rays of light that slowly began to shine on the walls could only mean one thing.

The young woman stirred and slowly rubbed her eyes. "Surely it can't be morning," she thought to herself. "Why, it seems I just fell asleep a few moments ago."

But the light in the room meant it was time to rise, and so she sat up, yawned, opened her eyes and…the sight before her made her back up against the wall in fright.

"Do not be afraid, Mary." The voice came from a light shining in the middle of the room—a light from which an angel spoke to her.

5

"Blessed are you among women," the angel said.

"Who-who are you?" Mary finally found the courage to ask.

"You have been chosen by God," the angel replied. "You will conceive and bear a Son and will name Him Jesus. He will be great and will be called the Son of the highest, and of His kingdom there will be no end."

"But how can this be?" Mary was confused. "I am a virgin."

"The Holy Spirit will come upon you and the holy one born will be called…the Son of God."

Suddenly, Mary was alone again. The light was gone, and so was the angel. Everything was just as it had been before she had gone to sleep that night, everything except that now she had been chosen by God to be the mother of His only Son. †

*A*fter Jesus was born in Bethlehem in Judea, during the time of King Herod, Magi from the east came to Jerusalem and asked, "Where is the one who has been born king of the Jews? We saw his star in the east and have come to worship him."

When King Herod heard this he was disturbed, and all Jerusalem with him. When he had called together all the people's chief priests and teachers of the law, he asked them where the Christ was to be born. "In Bethlehem in Judea," they replied, "for this is what the prophet has written:

"'But you, Bethlehem, in the land of Judah,
are by no means least among the rulers of Judah;
for out of you will come a ruler
who will be the shepherd of my people Israel.'"

Then Herod called the Magi secretly and found out from them the exact time the star had appeared. Matthew 2:1-7

South of Jerusalem, situated on a cone-like hill, stood Herodium, the palace-fortress of King Herod. Several stories high with intervals of square towers which were guarded twenty-four hours a day, the palace stood as a symbol of power, authority and the carefree ways of its wealthy occupants—but not on this night.

This particular night the palace did not ring out with its usual festive music or banquet chatter. No sound of laughter or fun traveled out among the hills. In its place were angry shouts, yelling and threats—threats so disgusting and evil even the king's advisor shuddered.

"But they are only children!" trembled the king's advisor as he trailed behind the expansive, flowing purple robes of a very impatient and angry Herod. Having given orders, the king made his way past a running group of soldiers he had just ordered on a mission, a mission that had the advisor trembling.

"And should that matter?" snapped the king. "*I* am the king of Israel! *I* am the king of the Jews! I will not share my throne with anyone else!"

"But it was only a prophecy!" squeaked the advisor, bowing so very low in respect he could scarcely see where he was going. "Perhaps…perhaps it is wrong!"

No sooner had the words poured out of his lips than the man was pressed against the wall. King Herod's grip was strong and his poor advisor could hardly breathe.

"What does the prophecy say?" the king managed through gritted teeth. The trembling counselor did his best to sputter out the ancient prophecy written in the Jewish scriptures 700 years before.

"B-b-but you, Bethlehem," quoted the man, "though you are little among the thousands of Judah…out of you shall come forth to me the one to be…to be…uh…to be…."

"To be…?" the king tightened his grip.

"The ruler of Israel!" blurted out the counselor.

"Argh!" grimaced King Herod and dragged the poor man outside to the balcony. "Tell me then! If the prophecy is wrong, what is THAT?"

Just beyond the king's pointing finger, in the midst of a star-strewn sky, was a light—a light that shone like no other in the heavens. It glimmered and sparkled very brightly—the majestic sign three important visitors from the eastern lands had recently inquired about.

"That star over Bethlehem—those astronomers said it announces the birth of the king of the Jews, did they not?" Then letting the advisor fall to the ground, the king stomped back into the great hall.

"*I* am the king of Israel! *I* am the king of the Jews! I will not share my throne with anyone else! Do you hear me? Not with anyone!"

And to the advisor's horror, galloping out from the palace gates below, mounted soldiers were already making their way to Bethlehem. There, under King Herod's orders, they would get rid of any threat to his throne by killing every male child under two years old.

Several miles away in the city of Bethlehem, a carpenter, his wife and young child slept peacefully in their house. The carpenter's name was Joseph and about eighteen months prior, his wife-to-be had shocked him with news that she was pregnant—news that had left him reeling.

Joseph agonized over his dilemma. What was he to make of Mary's wild claims?

"I am with child by the Holy Spirit," she had told him. "I have not been unfaithful to you."

After an evening of agonizing thought, he came to the conclusion that the best thing to do was follow Jewish law and call off the wedding. Exhausted and heartbroken, he prayed for God's guidance and soon after, fell into a deep sleep.

It was then that guidance came.

In a dream, an angel assured Joseph that Mary was indeed telling the truth and that he had been chosen to care for her and the child she carried. So clear was the message and so deep the peace that came upon him, the honest carpenter did not hesitate to take Mary as his wife.

True to the prophecies, the child had been born and true to God's requirement, Joseph had faithfully cared for the boy and his mother.

And so this night, months after the child's birth, as the little family rested, Joseph stirred in his sleep. Suddenly he awoke and sat bolt upright. Joseph's robe was soaked with sweat, and it took him a few moments to calm himself. He'd just had another dream, and the message was strong, clear and urgent. There was no time to lose.

"Mary! Quickly! We must go!"

Rubbing the sleep from her eyes, the young mother quickly made sure her little one was well. Then noticing that Joseph was gathering some belongings, she asked, "What is it? What are you doing?"

"Our Son," he replied. "He's in danger! We must leave— immediately!"

Outside the walls of the city, a large dust cloud seemed to be approaching from the east as Joseph, Mary and the child quickly moved through the narrow streets of the city toward one of the exit gates.

Keeping to the shadows and away from open areas, Joseph picked up his pace, leading the donkey that carried his family. He could see the guards were opening the gate as they usually did at dawn.

On the opposite side of the city, Herod's mounted soldiers arrived, thundering into the narrow streets lined with small shops and houses where the people were just waking up.

Joseph hurriedly made his way out of the city, just as the distant sounds of women's screams and children's cries began to grow. Puzzled by the awful noise, the guards ran to investigate.

The shrieking cries and desperate protests of parents trying to protect their screaming children grew as soldiers made their rounds from house to house, leaving small, defenseless children dying in pools of blood. Parents, those who had not been killed trying to protect their own, were heartbroken and swaying from shock.

Meanwhile, in the surrounding hills outside the city, Joseph and his family continued their escape, away from the land they knew so well, toward another land—one to which Joseph had been instructed by God to take the child and his mother for protection, where they would remain for many, many years to come.

Joseph, Mary and little Jesus made their way to Egypt. †

THE VOICE IN THE WILDERNESS

Taken from Matthew 3; Mark 1:2-13, Luke 3:3—4:13, John 1:19-34

> **"I** baptize you with water for repentance. But after me will come one who is more powerful than I, whose sandals I am not fit to carry. He will baptize you with the Holy Spirit and with fire." Matthew 3:11

The storm had passed, and from where the old prisoner sat in the cave, he could make out the moon reflected over a calmer sea. He moved a little closer to the fire.

"So the parents took the child and fled the country, sparing His life. How long were they gone?" asked the commander.

"Until King Herod died and an angel told them it was safe to return," replied the old prisoner as he rubbed some heat into his thin limbs. "They settled in a town called Nazareth. There they remained, the boy helping His father in carpentry work, growing, learning and…waiting."

"Waiting?" Titus looked up. "Waiting for what?"

"For the time appointed by God…the time when He would begin His ministry…years later, when He was a thirty-year-old man."

For a moment the old man was lost in thought, remembering a time long ago.

John had a hunger for God.

As soon as he heard that the prophet everyone was talking about was going to be nearby, he and his fishing partner, Andrew, decided it was more important to go hear him than to attend to their fishing business. Besides, both of them had brothers who were also partners, and John knew they could handle the work on their own.

What John didn't know was that they would end up spending several days with the Baptist, as the prophet was called. Along with preaching his message of repentance, the scraggly looking man also baptized people, submerging them in water as a symbol of leaving behind their old life and rising up into a new one.

The Baptist preached a strong message, encouraging people to turn away from their sins and to return to God's ways. While people flocked from all around to hear him, others were not equally impressed with the new prophet.

The Pharisees were a religious group that prided themselves on keeping the smallest demand of the Mosaic Law. Religious things were supposed to be done a "certain way" in their eyes, and everything had a rule. They certainly thought little of the Baptist and his wild way of preaching.

This day, as on many other occasions, two of them had come to question the Baptist and distract him from his work.

"Look, James, there they are again!" said John, pointing to the Pharisees who now stood on a hill, overlooking the river where the Baptist was doing his work.

People lined the shore; some were singing, others kneeling and praying, while still others waded through the current toward the Baptist, who was easy to spot with his tangled, long brown hair and his strong voice.

"REPENT!" he called out, as people drew near to be baptized. "Repent of your sins! Make your paths straight!

One after another, the people waded through the water toward the Baptist, confessing their sins and pleading for God's forgiveness.

"What shall we do to be saved?" one cried out as he made his way forward.

"Repent!" replied the Baptist. "If it is salvation you seek, then do as the scripture tells you: Prepare the way of the Lord! Make His paths straight!"

That people were flocking to this man and that he had the nerve to teach them was too much for the Pharisees to bear.

"What should you do to be saved?" the black-bearded Pharisee yelled, causing the Baptist and most of the people to turn his way. "What should you do to be saved? Follow the laws of Moses! That's what you should do! Go to the temp…"

"You vipers!" the Baptist interrupted, pointing a finger at the Pharisees. "REPENT!" Slowly, he turned back to continue his work as more people waded into the water.

It took a moment for the Pharisee to recover. "You're asking *us* to repent? We who keep the laws of Moses more carefully than the likes of all of you?" the Pharisee motioned to the masses around him. "REPENTENCE FROM WHAT?"

The Baptist stopped his work. Then he turned so rapidly the Pharisee, who was a good and safe distance away, took a slight step back. With one sweeping comment the Pharisee had passed judgment on everyone around him, and the Baptist was not one to keep silent. Outraged, he waded through the water toward the Pharisee.

"You think you are acceptable to God just because you have Abraham for your father," his voice boomed, as he swiftly picked up two rocks. Fearing the worst, the Pharisees scuttled backwards, nearly losing their footing.

"God is able to raise up children for Himself from these stones!" roared the Baptist, as he threw the rocks back into the river, turned and walked toward the waiting people.

As long as the Baptist was walking away from him, the black-bearded Pharisee plucked up some courage. "Tell us plainly! Do you claim to be the Christ? The Messiah? The one God is sending to save us?"

The Baptist slowly turned to the Pharisees. "I am the voice of one crying in the wilderness, prepare the way of the Lord. I baptize you with water, but He who will come after me is more powerful than I. I am not even worthy to untie His sandals."

So much attention had been given to the conversation between the Baptist and the Pharisees, no one had noticed the quiet, humble man who stepped into the water, slowly made His way toward the Baptist, and now stood, waiting patiently behind him.

The Baptist continued to address the Pharisees, "The One that comes after me will baptize you with…." He stopped mid-sentence.

John and Andrew, who had been watching the Pharisees, realized the Baptist had not finished his fiery message. Curious, they turned to him.

The Baptist looked stunned for a moment, but he managed to finish his sentence. "The One who comes after me…He will baptize you…with…the Holy Spirit and with fire."

Then he turned around and faced the quiet man. "It…it is You!" the Baptist whispered. The quiet man simply looked at him, then at the water.

"I can't baptize You!" The boldness faded from the Baptist's face. "It is I who should be baptized by You."

Jesus smiled. "It is God's will we are here to fulfill, not our own."

The Pharisees were nearly falling over the top of the hill, trying to hear what was being said. They didn't quite understand what was going on, but they were offended that the Baptist had turned his back on them, giving all his attention to the man with whom he spoke.

John and Andrew looked at each other. They also did not understand what was happening. All they knew was that the Baptist had never behaved the way he did now. John didn't catch every word, but he saw the man in front of the Baptist being submerged under the current.

Although nothing was out of the ordinary about this baptism, at the same time something was very unique about it. That's what John thought, but the baptism was nothing compared to what he witnessed next.

No sooner had the man emerged from the water than the gray clouds seemed to shift, the sun broke through and then... there was a Voice from heaven, and God said, "This is My beloved Son."

The Voice was so clear John turned to see if someone behind him had spoken. But the only person behind him was Andrew, and he continued to stare in the direction of the Baptist.

"We've heard enough!" yelled the Pharisee, disrupting John's thoughts.

"Yes! Plenty in fact! I am sure the High Priest will be interested in our little visit with you!" added the elder Pharisee, as the two turned and walked away, trying very hard to avoid any contact with the "common" people.

John turned to look in the direction Andrew was gazing. The Baptist still stood motionless, watching the quiet man walking away in the distance, but not in the direction of the other people or the city. In fact, Jesus seemed to be heading quite the opposite way—straight toward the desert. †

*T*hen *Jesus was led by the *Spirit* into the desert to be tempted by the devil.*
Matthew 4:1

The sizzling sun burned down on the desolate Judean desert where Jesus had been fasting for forty days. His lips, parched and cracked…His tongue swollen from thirst…He was weary, dirty and tired.

"Forty days," came a whispered voice. "Impressive!"

The voice was not the one at Jesus' baptism—the voice of His Father: caring, encouraging. It was a different sort of voice—one that carried in it a cold, mocking and unkind emotion—the voice of His enemy.

"You must be hungry…so very hungry," the voice hissed around Jesus. "Here's a thought. If You truly are the Son of God…turn these stones into bread."

The tempter turned Jesus' attention to a pile of rocks nearby, and they slowly faded into an image of soft, fresh bread. Delicious bread.

"Satisfy Yourself!" the voice whispered.

Jesus closed His eyes. "It is written: 'Man shall not live by bread alone but by every word that proceeds from the mouth of God!'"

The tempter was pained and for a moment groaned.

Jesus stood.

Suddenly the voice returned: angry, persistent. The ground shook, the sand burst, circling Jesus in a horrendous cyclone that just as quickly disappeared—and when it did, Jesus was standing on the highest point of the temple. The wind was howling. The people below looked tiny.

"If You are the Son of God," the voice whispered, "throw Yourself down! No harm can come to You for it is written: 'He will command His angels, and they will lift you up in their hands so that you don't dash even your foot against a stone!' Do it! Throw Yourself down!" The voice laughed.

"It is also written: 'Do not put the Lord your God to the test!'" Jesus replied.

The devil cried out in a mixture of frustration and agonizing pain.

The temple was gone and Jesus now stood atop a high mountain. As far as the eye could see there were glorious palaces, armies of soldiers, all the kingdoms of the world and their splendor.

"All this I will give You," he said, "if You will bow down and worship me!"

Jesus said to him: "Away from me, Satan! For it is written: 'Worship the Lord your God, and serve Him only.'"

The devil shrieked—a mixture of agony, frustration and utter, gnawing pain that rose to a deafening roar—and then was silenced completely.

A few moments later Jesus made His way back to the city where He would begin the work He had been sent to do. †

THE FISHERMEN

Taken from Matthew 4:18-22; Mark 1:16-20; Luke 4:5-7; John 1:35-41

*T*he next day John [the Baptist] was there again with two of his disciples. When he saw Jesus passing by, he said, "Look, the Lamb of God!"

When the two disciples heard him say this, they followed Jesus. Turning around, Jesus saw them following and asked, "What do you want?"

They said, "Rabbi" (which means Teacher), "where are you staying?"

"Come," he replied, "and you will see."

So they went and saw where he was staying, and spent that day with him. It was about the tenth hour.

Andrew, Simon Peter's brother, was one of the two who heard what John had said and who had followed Jesus. The first thing Andrew did was to find his brother Simon and tell him, "We have found the Messiah" (that is, the Christ). John 1:35-41

Bursting with excitement, John ran toward the Sea of Galilee where he could see a boat making its way back to the shore. Though still a distance away, he could hear the gruff complaints of one of the fishermen—Simon, an impatient man and partner in a fishing business.

"A complete waste of time!" Simon roared. "All night at sea and what have we got to show for it?"

"Well, a temper it seems! Cheer up, Simon, you'll be off to your comfortable bed soon," joked his co-worker, James.

"And if it wasn't bad enough, those two brothers of ours are nowhere to be found!" Simon grumbled, jumping into the water and pulling the boat to shore. He was still complaining loudly when, to his surprise, John and Andrew jumped into the water to help him with his chore.

"Simon! James!" John greeted them excitedly.

"Now's a fine time to show up!" James scolded. "We've got a business to run, little brother! Or have you forgotten?"

"There's a good reason we're late!" exclaimed John, bursting with news. "We found Him!"

James' puzzled look and Simon's angrier glance demanded an explanation.

"We found the Messiah!" John beamed. "The Baptist told us to follow Him, and we did! In fact, we've been talking with Him all night!"

Simon struggled to keep from doing something he would later regret; the fact that their co-workers and brothers were on some mysterious mission made no difference to him, especially when their business was affected.

Throwing down the nets in anger, Simon began to shove John.

"We've got a business to run and you two have nothing better to do than to waste your time on some…." Simon stopped speaking suddenly, annoyed by a stranger who had approached them and now stood watching. "And who are You?"

But before the man could answer, John explained. "This is the one I told you about, Simon. The Messiah: Jesus of Nazareth!"

Simon stared at the man who simply stared right back at him and smiled. Something about Him held Simon's gaze. Something made it difficult to look away and somehow…Simon's anger quickly disappeared. Still, Simon was no fool. Unlike his brother who wanted to find the Messiah, Simon was simply concerned with making a living.

Maybe it was his lack of sleep or maybe the thought that the long-awaited Messiah could be this quiet Nazarene standing before him—or maybe it was a combination of both. Simon burst into uncontrollable laughter.

"The Messiah we have been waiting for?" he managed in between a knee-slap and holding his sides. "Jesus of Nazareth?"

"Take the boat out, Simon," Jesus said calmly.

Why such a simple statement would demand everyone's sudden and unswerving attention was unbelievable, but all four of the fishermen, Simon included, suddenly fastened their eyes on Jesus. Simon's laughter quickly quieted, and he looked over at Jesus.

"You want a catch, don't you?" Jesus asked.

"We've been fishing all night! We've caught nothing…" Simon began.

"Come on, Simon! What have you got to lose?" John exclaimed, as he ran toward the boat.

Simon stood there, watching as Jesus headed to the boat. James shrugged his shoulders and made his way to the boat, helping Andrew with the nets along the way.

"Alright, I'm coming! But only to get this nonsense out of your heads once and for all!" Simon said, helping to push the boat back into the water. He added, "And you two will be doing all the work next week! You got that?"

Then, jumping into the boat, they rowed toward the middle of the sea.

When the fishermen had taken the boat out a little way, Jesus spoke. "Lower the nets here."

Having spent a good part of the night talking with Jesus, John and Andrew had no problem following His instructions. They knew something was very special about this man and trusted Him to be the Messiah. Eagerly they picked up the nets and threw them overboard where they sank beneath the water.

Simon, on the other hand, simply slumped down on the floor of the ship, yawning.

"This is a waste of time," he muttered. "A complete waste of…."

The boat shook and tilted to one side.

Caught off guard, John grabbed hold of the mast while some of the others held onto the side, trying not to fall overboard.

"What was…?" Simon gasped, now wide-awake.

The boat shook again, the nets causing it to tilt even further on its side.

"Simon!" James shouted, as he peered into the water. "Come look at this!" Then seeing that Simon just sat like he had been turned to stone, James yelled, "LOOK!"

It was all they could do to keep the boat balanced, and Simon nearly fell over the edge as he looked into the water. His eyes widened. His jaw dropped. Exhaustion was gone, and his heart began to beat so wildly he was shaking.

"There are too many fish!" John exclaimed. "The nets are breaking!"

James, Andrew and John were trying to pull the catch into the boat as fast as they could, before the nets unraveled.

Nearly numb with shock, Simon grabbed hold of the net, and together they heaved the large catch of fish into the boat. Simon fell backwards as a downpour of flopping and wriggling fish spilled on top of him. His mouth opened as if to say something, but nothing came out.

James raised his hand to his head. "It's a miracle!" he shouted. "A miracle!" Andrew sat down, laughing. And John, overcome with emotion, made his way toward Jesus and fell to his knees. Bursting with joy, he exclaimed. "Lord! My Lord!"

Jesus watched them all, and smiled. †

"Come, follow me," Jesus said, "and I will make you fishers of men." At once they left their nets and followed him. Matthew 4:19-20

John set the last overflowing basket of fish down off his shoulders and wiped the sweat off his brow. He leaned on a nearby boat to give his back some rest, still shaky from the events of the last hour—the almost unbelievable last hour.

"How is it possible," he wondered to himself, "that someone could make fish swim by the hundreds into a net?" But that was exactly what Jesus had done, evident by the throngs of people eagerly buying up their catch. *Why would Jesus do something like that?* he pondered. *What was the purpose? Was there a meaning?*

His thoughts were suddenly interrupted by the excitement of James and Andrew, doing their best to keep up with the swarm of customers.

"This is the largest catch we've ever had!" exclaimed James, as he tossed an empty basket to the side and hauled in a full one.

"And the biggest sale!" added Andrew, counting the coins in his hand. "Next!"

They were excited and happy, and watching them in action made John chuckle. Simon, however, sat apart, watching the sale of fish for a moment and then turning to look at Jesus who sat by Himself further away. John could tell by the way Simon looked at Jesus that there were a million questions going through his head. After a while he stood up, and slowly made his way to Jesus.

"Lord," Simon kept his gaze low, preferring to keep his eyes on the ground. "Lord, please leave me. I...I am a sinful man."

It was quite a sight to see Simon so humble, so downcast—so opposite of the man John knew.

"Don't be afraid, Simon," Jesus replied.

The words seemed more like a command than a reply, John thought, for immediately Simon was at ease and finally gazed directly at Jesus.

"Follow Me," Jesus added, and then He turned to John and the others. "All of you, follow Me and I will make you fishers of men."

He didn't speak loudly. He didn't have to. There was something about the way Jesus spoke that commanded attention. John immediately moved in closer, as did Andrew, leaving James to continue his sales.

Simon hardly knew what to say, so as usual, he simply asked the first thing that came into his head. Half-knowing the answer already, he asked, "You mean, now? Follow You, just like that?"

Jesus didn't answer—at least not with words. He simply stood up and smiled.

The silence was a bit overwhelming for Simon, so he just had to add, "But, this is the biggest catch we've ever had!"

Jesus looked at him and said, "You are Simon, son of John. You will be called Peter. And from now on," Jesus said, "you will catch men." And with that He turned and walked away.

Peter, John and Andrew stood shocked. The invitation…no…the call was clear. There was no mistaking what Jesus meant.

Peter stood motionless for a moment, then took a step toward one of his boats. Leaning on it, he passed his hand over the rough wood, looked over at his other boats, the nets, the full baskets. Then finally he turned his eyes to John and Andrew.

He didn't say a word. He simply took a few steps backward, and giving his workplace one last look, turned and began following Jesus—at first walking, then sprinting and finally breaking into a full run.

John and Andrew didn't waste a minute. Looking at each other, they simply nodded, laughed joyfully and went after Peter, whooping in freedom they had not felt in a very long time.

"Well?" James, who had just witnessed his friends and business partners walk away from the most profitable day of their lives, was brought back to the moment by a woman who was waiting for her fish with hand outstretched.

"Well what are you waiting for?" the woman demanded. "Where's my fish?"

James stood, looked at the fish, the money, and the customers still eager to buy.

"I said, where's my fish!" growled the woman.

Glancing at Jesus and his friends in the distance, James muttered to himself, "This will be very bad for business. Very bad!" Then turning to the sour-faced woman, he added, "Here's your fish!" putting several into her hands. "And here! And here and there…" he said pointing to the rest of the baskets. "You can have them all!"

And to her surprise and that of the crowd, James turned and ran as fast as he could to follow Jesus along with his friends, leaving the boats, the nets, the fish, the money and a puzzled group of people far, far behind. †

HEALING

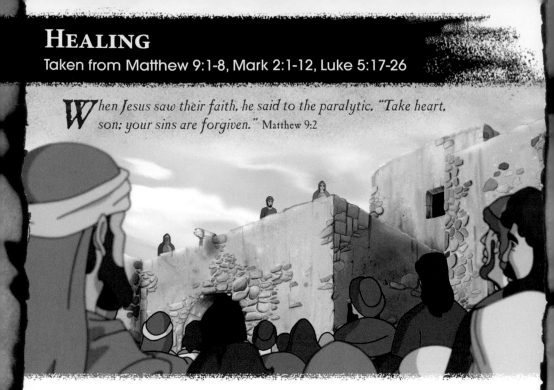

When Jesus saw their faith, he said to the paralytic, "Take heart, son; your sins are forgiven." Matthew 9:2

John couldn't step back any farther. Peter's house was overflowing with people who had gathered to hear Jesus speak. News of the miracle of fish had spread quickly, along with the stories of additional miracles in which Jesus had healed a man possessed by an evil spirit and restored Peter's bed-ridden mother-in-law back to health instantly.

Now so many people had gathered they spilled out into the street. Even some Pharisees were in the crowd, curious to know more about the miracle-worker. The room was silent except for the voice of Jesus until a loud pounding interrupted Him, followed by an ear-splitting snap.

John thought a wall was giving way due to the number of people crammed into the room. Then he heard Peter's cry of alarm. "The roof! What are you doing to my roof?"

In a far corner of the room, people stumbled over each other, covering their heads as bits of clay and branches began to tumble down. No sooner had Peter made his way through the frightened people than to his utter shock, part of the roof suddenly caved in, filling the place with dust. Coughing and shaking fragments of mud from his hair, Peter's temper flared until he heard a faint, pitiful plea.

"Help me," the feeble voice trembled. "Please! Help me!"

At first it was hard to tell where the voice was coming from until, to everyone's surprise, a mat was lowered down.

"Please. Help me," came the cry once again.

The closest people rushed to help, gently placing the bundle onto the floor. The sight left Peter speechless. On the mat lay a man, his limbs twisted in all directions, unable to move—a paralytic.

Several of his friends jumped down through the roof and rushed to Jesus, begging him on the man's behalf.

"He's been this way for years! We heard You could do miracles. Please, is there anything You can do for him? Anything!" they begged.

Jesus walked over to the paralyzed man, who did his best to look at Jesus, trying to follow Him with his eyes, though he couldn't turn his head.

"Please!" he whimpered.

While it was obvious the man was asking for the impossible, everyone was touched by his desperate pleas for relief. Even one of the Pharisees, annoyed in part by the importance placed upon Jesus, could only bring himself to scold the sick man ever so gently—a virtue rarely shown by their group.

"Now, now, what can the good teacher do?" the Pharisee reasoned. Turning to the man's friends, he added, "Take this man home!"

But the paralytic only cried out the more, until…Jesus knelt down beside him.

The paralytic immediately quieted down, gazing at Jesus and not taking his eyes off Him.

Jesus smiled. "Your sins," He declared, "are forgiven."

For a few seconds there was total silence, soon followed by gasps, whispering and murmuring from the crowd. Eyes widened, jaws dropped. John nervously looked over at Peter, who simply shook his head in disbelief. Some people looked in the direction of the Pharisees, waiting for their reaction, but the Pharisees seemed stunned—caught off guard. One of them tried to speak, but his jaw only trembled.

The shocking moment was broken at last by the stuttering, whispered exclamation of the trembling Pharisee. "Blasphemy!" The Pharisee was shaking with anger. "BLASPHEMY! Only God can forgive sins, and it's an insult to God to say otherwise!" he proclaimed. "Only God…."

Jesus stood up, looking straight into the eyes of the Pharisee. The man was so startled by His gaze he fell silent.

"Tell Me," Jesus asked, "which is easier to say: your sins are forgiven, or get up and walk?"

Puzzled, the Pharisee simply stood silent.

"But to show you that I have also been given power to forgive sins…." Jesus turned to the paralytic, stretched out His arms and said, "Arise, take up your bed and walk."

Once again, there was utter silence. No one moved. No one spoke. And then—the paralyzed man gasped.

All eyes turned to the poor man. His head tilted back, his eyes closed and slowly, ever so slowly, his head began to move, at first to one side then to the other followed by a movement in his fingers, then his hands, his toes, his feet, his forearms and legs. Then gently, almost rhythmically, his limbs untangled, moving from side to side, wriggling, moving in ways they had not done in years.

By the time the man stood up, the astonished people had backed up so much he had ample room to run around. Overjoyed, he hugged Jesus, loudly thanking Him.

All John could do was laugh, his heart overflowing with joy. Peter sat down to avoid collapsing, and Andrew and James shook their heads in wonder, their eyes filling with tears.

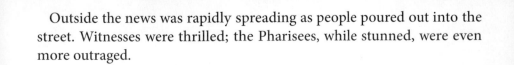

Outside the news was rapidly spreading as people poured out into the street. Witnesses were thrilled; the Pharisees, while stunned, were even more outraged.

"A miracle!" a woman gasped, as she stopped passersby. "I just witnessed a miracle!"

But one of the Pharisees decided to put a stop to her excitement then and there. He grabbed the woman by the arm, spinning her around to face him. "Healing a man is one thing," he scolded her. "But forgiving sins? No one can forgive sins but God!"

Then pushing her aside, he made his way to another group of Pharisees, whispering angrily and pointing to the house where Jesus still remained.

Inside the house, the paralytic, Jesus' followers, and the remaining people surrounded Jesus. "The time has come," He preached. "The kingdom of heaven is here. Believe the good news of the forgiveness of sins available to everyone!" †

He replied, "Whether he is a sinner or not, I don't know. One thing I do know. I was blind but now I see!" John 9:25

"I tell you He's a troublemaker and nothing but a nuisance, this Jesus of Nazareth!" the white-bearded Pharisee spat out.

Several of the Pharisees were holding an emergency conference to discuss the rising popularity of Jesus of Nazareth.

"Publicans, tax collectors, pro-stitutes…saying He can forgive sins!" continued the speaker.

"Blasphemy! That's exactly what He is guilty of!" some of the others joined in.

"Then what are we waiting for?" retorted the speaker, getting very red in the face. "We are the keepers of the law of Moses. It is our responsibility to stop Him. We *must* take action!"

At this suggestion the room erupted into many discussions, silenced only by a calm yet commanding voice.

"And yet, you have seen His works," a dignified-looking Pharisee with a long gray beard spoke out. "He heals the sick…why, I've heard He's even raised the dead."

"Oh please!" the black-bearded Pharisee jumped to his feet, attempting to take the floor. "A sick boy gets well and suddenly you have the dead raised to life! People talk, rumors grow!"

"But just today," continued his dignified counterpart, "a blind man regained his sight. Here, in this very temple!

"Or so they say!" interjected another Pharisee. "How do we know that these so called miracles are real?"

The gray-bearded Pharisee was about to offer his opinion when a temple guard, accompanied by a beggarly man and a nervous older couple, interrupted him.

"Sir, this is the man you were asking about."

"It's a miracle, I tell you!" the beggar blurted out. "I can see! I can…."

But his excitement was cut short. One of the Pharisees had signaled the guard, who in turn had muffled the man's mouth with his hand. The poor man tried very hard to continue his story, while pulling on the guard's hand at the same time.

"What is the meaning of this? Bringing these people here!" demanded one of the Pharisees.

The gray-bearded Pharisee merely raised his hand calmly. "Indulge me for a moment, please." Turning to the squirming man's parents, he asked, "Tell me. Is this your son?"

The old couple simply nodded; being brought before the religious authorities could have bad consequences, and they were terrified to say anything that could be misunderstood.

"And was he born blind?" continued the gray-bearded Pharisee.

The old couple merely nodded again.

"How is it that he sees now?" inquired the Pharisee, trying as best he could to put them at ease.

The poor couple could not get away with a nod this time, so the husband replied, "Our son is old enough to answer for himself," he trembled. "Uh…why don't you ask him?"

Impatient with his counterpart's more gentle ways, the white-bearded Pharisee approached the guard, giving him permission to free the couple's son.

"What have you got to say for yourself?" the Pharisee demanded.

"A man…a prophet…He healed me and now, now I can see!" exclaimed the man. "It's a miracle I tell you!"

"If you can see, it's by a work of God and not this man you talk about—one we know is a sinner!" came the Pharisee's reply.

"A sinner?" the thought seemed to baffle the man for a moment. "Whether He is a sinner or not, I don't know. The only thing I am sure of is that once I was blind and now…now I can see!"

"But how?" stomped the Pharisee. "How did He heal you? How?"

"I-I don't know," replied the man. "But I am sure we can find Him." And then a thought came to him, and he broke into a huge, somewhat toothless, grin. "Do you also want to be His disciples?"

The thought that any Pharisee would want to be the disciple of the carpenter of Nazareth was enough to make the Pharisee's blood boil.

"Out!" he ordered. "Get him out of my sight!"

The guards immediately grabbed the former blind man and quickly threw him out. As the poor man lay on the ground rubbing his legs, the Pharisees came to the door.

"You were cursed with blindness and yet you dare to teach us?" yelled the Pharisee. Then turning to a guard, he added, "Get him out! NOW!"

The guards quickly grabbed the man by his arms, dragging him away as he continued to marvel at all the new things around him, which he was unable to appreciate when he was blind.

"I can see you and you!" he exclaimed to the guards. "And the sky, the birds, the clouds! I am healed! Healed!"

And they cast him out of the temple, closing the doors behind him and leaving him outside, where he continued to tell others, "I was blind but now…now I see!" †

*"**I** am sending you out like sheep among wolves."* Matthew 10:16

It was very early in the morning, and the sun was not yet visible above the horizon. A refreshing chill stirred in the morning air as John cooked a breakfast of fish on an open fire, with the help of Peter.

On the grassy area where they had spent the night, several men still slept soundly while others were just waking up. They were twelve now—twelve men handpicked by Jesus to be His disciples.

Jesus had grown so much in popularity He could hardly eat without being surrounded by people, begging for a blessing or for healing. So some evenings, He would lead the twelve into the countryside away from the crowds, where they could rest, and He could sit a little distance away to pray.

Sometimes Jesus would spend all night in prayer. That night had been no different, and now John watched as Jesus remained where He had been all night, still praying, still talking with His Father in heaven.

The thought made John realize how much his life had changed from the life of a fisherman to a "fisher of men," as Jesus had put it.

John brought his attention back to the cooking. "Do you ever miss it?" John asked.

"Miss what?" Peter asked.

"Home…Galilee…" John replied.

Peter thought about it a while and then answered, "Sometimes—the boat, the open sea, my family." Then he added with a smirk, "But not my wife's cooking! That I don't miss."

They laughed.

"Then you'll appreciate it more when we go back," John replied, as he handed Peter a fish and placed more on the fire. "Don't you think?"

Peter didn't respond right away. Then he said, "We're not going back, John."

John stopped his cooking and looked over at Peter.

"You know as well as I do that we will never go back," Peter added. "God is doing something special…different. We're never going back, John—not to our homes, our families or our friends."

What Peter said was true. John knew that but none of the twelve had ever actually put it into words. God had called them. Going forward, leaving their old life was what they were doing.

"I am sending you on a journey," Jesus' voice jolted John back from his thoughts. Jesus stood before them now and motioned the others to gather around Him.

"I am sending the twelve of you on a journey," Jesus continued. "Peter, Andrew, James, John, Philip, Bartholomew, Thomas, Matthew, James, Thaddeus, Simon and Judas. You will travel two-by-two and go into different parts of the country to share the good news that the kingdom of heaven is near."

Peter stepped forward. This would be their first mission, and he wanted Jesus to know he understood what was expected of them.

"Lord," Peter said, "we have left everything to follow You!"

"Yes, Peter," Jesus said as He smiled. "And anyone who has left houses, or brothers, or sisters, or father or mother or wife or children or lands for My sake and the sake of the Gospel will receive 100 times more, with persecution, and in the end eternal life!"

Jesus walked among them, speaking to each individual disciple. "Heal the sick…raise the dead…cure those who have demons. God has given to you freely, so freely give!"

The disciples looked at each other in astonishment. They were very excited. Jesus was sending them out to bless the people. Their mission would be wonderful and challenging, but Jesus was giving them the power to do the very things He did. They thought of all the people they could help.

"But be careful. I send you out as sheep among wolves, so be as wise as a serpent but as harmless as a dove because not everyone will receive you."

It was a good warning, John thought to himself. They were going out to represent Jesus, and no doubt they would be treated like Him. Some people would be happy to receive them, and others would not.

"If you confess Me before men," Jesus continued, "I will also confess you before My Father in heaven. But whoever denies Me before men, I will deny before My Father in heaven.

"And keep this in mind, all of you," Jesus said as He placed His arms around the shoulders of the two nearest Him. The others gathered closer, and soon they were all shoulder-to-shoulder in a circle. "He who finds his life will lose it. But if you lose your life for My sake," He smiled broadly, "you will find it!"

John could not take his eyes off Jesus, for His face was beaming with joy.

A few hours later, the disciples left camp two-by-two, traveling into parts of the country they had never seen. Weeks later they would return, bearing the same joy Jesus had shown, rejoicing at the way God had worked through them! †

FORGIVEN
Taken from Matthew 4:25, John 8:1-11

"*If any one of you is without sin, let him be the first to throw a stone at her.*" John 8:7

As the Pharisees held council, the doors to their chambers flew open and in stomped the white-bearded Pharisee, trembling with fury.

"Galilee, the Decapolis, Jerusalem…even across the Jordan!" he shouted. "It's as if the whole world is following Jesus of Nazareth!"

"And you just now noticed?" answered the black-bearded Pharisee sarcastically.

"Well, we can't very well just continue to sit here doing nothing!" the white-bearded Pharisee retorted. "What is He doing that draws so many people to Him? What is it that…?"

"Sir!" The Pharisee's rant was interrupted by one of the temple guards who marched into the room with some urgency.

"What is it?" spat the angry Pharisee. "Can't you see we are in counsel?"

"Forgive my interruption," the guard bowed, "but a group of people have caught a woman…in the very act of adultery, they say."

Frustrated by what he considered an interruption to more important matters, the Pharisee simply brushed him away. "What of it? You know the law. Have her stoned!"

Accepting the command, the guard made his way to the door while the Pharisee tried to collect his thoughts.

"Uh…where was I? Ah yes! What are we going to do about this Jesus? He's taking the people away from our influence! We can't just…."

"Wait!" The black-bearded Pharisee was on his feet, gesturing for the guard to come back into the room.

This second interruption did not please the white-bearded Pharisee, who was outraged to be cut off mid-sentence once again. "How dare you interrupt me!" he spewed. "I am talking about something very important!"

But the black-bearded Pharisee was too preoccupied with an idea to be bothered by his hot-tempered colleague. Turning to the guard, he ordered, "The woman caught in adultery… bring her with you and come with us!"

"But…!" protested the outraged white-bearded Pharisee until the other put an end to his outburst.

"Will you be quiet!" the black-bearded Pharisee shouted. "I have an idea. Jesus opens the eyes of the blind, doesn't He? We too shall open the eyes of these blind followers of His! Now, keep quiet and come with me!"

The white-bearded Pharisee had no choice but to follow the other Pharisees out the door and into the street.

John was always amazed by how people hung on to every word Jesus said. As they sat outside near a temple wall, John watched as the large group of people Jesus was teaching sat quietly, smiles on their faces. Jesus had a wonderful way of making people feel the presence of God, and John felt honored to have been chosen as one of His closest followers.

He was enjoying sitting near Jesus and listening to Him, until a commotion nearby drew his attention. Without so much as an "excuse me," a group of Pharisees shoved their way through the crowd, dragging a sobbing woman behind them. With little care, they pushed her toward Jesus. Surprised by the interruption, those closest to the front moved back.

The woman's clothes were partly torn, and she looked a mess—no doubt from the rough way she had been treated. Too ashamed to look up, she kept her gaze to the ground and wept.

The black-bearded Pharisee, who had thrown the woman on the ground, stepped up to Jesus.

"Uh, Rabbi," said the Pharisee, though not in the way most people used the term. There was no real show of respect when he called Jesus that. "Rabbi, this woman was caught in adultery—or rather, privately with a man she is not married to."

No sooner had the Pharisee accused her, than the people began to whisper among themselves, drawing as far away from her as possible.

The Pharisee went on, "Now, Rabbi, You know the Law of Moses commands that such a woman…" and he stooped to pick up a very large rock, "should be stoned."

Holding out the rock to Jesus, the Pharisee smiled. "But, Rabbi…what do You say?"

John understood what the Pharisee was up to. If Jesus did not stone the woman, He would publicly be rejecting the Laws of Moses. If He stoned her, then He would publicly be siding with the Pharisees.

The other Pharisees smiled. They too understood the plan, and bent down to pick up stones. Very soon, the majority of the people had stones in their hands, ready to put the woman to death.

All eyes were on Jesus, who kept silent, His eyes fixed on the woman who sobbed quietly as she awaited her punishment.

The black-bearded Pharisee smiled, confident he had put Jesus in a very uncomfortable situation. He turned and gave his companions a knowing look.

Slowly, Jesus stooped to the ground, but to the Pharisee's surprise, He didn't pick up a rock.

John watched as with slow, deliberate movements, Jesus began to write in the dirt with His finger. John couldn't make out what He was writing, since it was visible only to the accusing Pharisee. What John did notice, however, was that the Pharisee's expression began to change slowly. His proud smile began to disappear, replaced by a look of shock. He began to look very pale, and he seemed to shake in fear. Sweat poured down his face, and he looked around, trying to see if anyone else could read what Jesus had written.

John watched as Jesus finished writing, and looked up at the Pharisees.

"Whoever is without sin," Jesus spoke calmly, "let him be the first one to throw a stone at her."

The Pharisee swayed for a moment, took a step back and dropped the rock he was holding.

No one spoke. The only sound was the woman's muffled whimpering, and then…the sound of a rock hitting the ground, then another, and another, and then more. Without so much as a word, people were dropping their stones, turning and walking away.

The Pharisee tried to regain his composure; then with one quick look of anger and contempt at Jesus, he turned and left, pushing his companions out of the way as he did so. The rest of the Pharisees quickly followed him, whispering as they went.

When only His closest followers remained, Jesus turned to the woman. "Where are your accusers?" He asked gently. "Isn't anyone condemning you?"

The frightened woman raised her head slowly, wiping the tears from her eyes as she looked around. No one was to her left. Slowly she turned the opposite direction—no one was there either. At last, she looked at Jesus, still trembling, and surrounded only by the stones her accusers had left behind.

"No one, Sir," she replied.

Jesus leaned closer, looked into her eyes, and said, "I do not condemn you either. Go and sin no more."

For a moment she stood there, simply staring at Jesus, grateful…humbled. "Thank You," she said before turning toward the narrow street that led to her home.

John and the other disciples marveled at how Jesus had handled the entire situation. As Jesus got up and walked away, they picked up their things and followed Him. †

THE SECRET BELIEVER
Taken from John 3:1-21

"I tell you the truth, no one can see the kingdom of God unless he is born again." John 3:3

It was late in the evening, and John was very tired. He yawned, wrapped a thin blanket around his shoulders and leaned back against a tree. The other disciples were a short distance away, gathered around a fire, some sitting and talking and others already fast asleep.

Life in the company of Jesus was exciting, and every day was a new adventure. Settling in for a good night's rest, John thought back on the activity of the last few days: preaching to crowds of hundreds and the healing of ten lepers—even a dead girl was raised back to life. They never really knew what would happen next—not even where they would be sleeping each night. Many nights they simply slept where they could—sometimes outside, just like they were doing this night.

Yes, following Jesus is exciting…and exhausting, he thought to himself as he made himself comfortable and closed his eyes.

SNAP!

The sound of someone stepping on a branch startled John, and immediately he leaped to his feet.

"Who's there?" he called out. "Who is…?"

A shadowy figure stepped out from the dark forest. Mist had slowly begun to rise, making it difficult for John to see the person's identity.

"Master Nicodemus!" exclaimed John, as he recognized the man.

"I have come to see the rabbi," the old Pharisee explained.

Jesus sat off to one side, away from His followers. It was His custom to spend time alone, praying.

Motioning to Jesus, Nicodemus approached Him respectfully and then sat down. Jesus turned His attention to the Pharisee, welcoming Him with a smile and a nod.

"Rabbi…" began Nicodemus. "Rabbi, I believe You are a man sent by God because it would be impossible for anyone to do the miracles You do were it not for God."

"The truth is," Jesus said, "no one can experience the kingdom of God unless he is born again."

"Born again?" Nicodemus inquired. "But—how can someone be born again when he is old?"

"The flesh gives birth to the flesh," explained Jesus. "And the Spirit… the Spirit gives birth to the spirit."

Nicodemus was confused. "But…how can this be?" he asked.

"You are a teacher of Israel, and you don't understand these things?" Jesus asked. "No one goes to heaven except He who came from heaven. You see, God loved the world so much that He sent His only Son so that anyone who believes in Him will have eternal life. God sent His Son to save the world, not to condemn it."

Then He leaned forward, placing His hand on Nicodemus' shoulder.

"You must be born again, Nicodemus…in your heart." †

"*This bread is my flesh, which I will give for the life of the world.*"
John 6:51

Titus stoked the fire as the commander poured water into a cup and offered it to the old prisoner. It was the first gesture of kindness the old man had been shown in a very long time, and he drank the water gratefully.

"So Jesus was a teacher and a healer of the sick, and the sick at heart," noted the commander. "Even some of your religious leaders sought His opinion—a popular man, it seems to me."

"And His fame spread," the old prisoner continued with his story. "People came from all around to hear Him, to fill their hearts…as well as their stomachs."

"What do you mean?" asked Titus.

"Well, the crowds numbered in the thousands and often stayed until the evening. On one occasion, knowing the people were hungry and had nowhere to go for food, Jesus took two fish and five loaves of bread and with that fed over 5,000 people. Another time He fed over 4,000 with a few fish and seven loaves of bread."

"What?" exclaimed the commander. "How is that possible?"

"A miracle," replied the old prisoner. "Jesus prayed and the fish and bread were miraculously multiplied. Every person in that crowd was fed to their heart's content. We even had food left over. After that miracle, the people wanted to crown Him king of Israel!"

"I can still hear them now…" he remembered, as he closed his eyes and leaned against the rocky wall.

Having eaten the loaves and fish, a multitude of people rushed toward Jesus and His disciples, calling out praises and adoration.

"This is the prophet who is to come!" someone shouted.

"Who else could do these miracles and speak with such authority!" another added.

"Jesus is the Messiah! The one we have been waiting for!" praised another. More and more people took up the praises until some began to suggest crowning Jesus the king of Israel.

John and his companions were thrilled by the reception; their hearts filled with delight and pride. After all, they were the closest to Jesus. While they took in all the praise and recognition, however, Jesus turned

and walked away from the crowd and into the woods. The disciples followed Him.

"Lord! Listen to that!" said Judas excitedly, while trying to keep pace with Jesus. "Everyone adores You! And not only here but all over the country! Now is the time to go on to Jerusalem!"

"Yes," replied Jesus.

John was thrilled to hear this, as were the rest of the disciples. Jesus was wildly popular. If they could secure His popularity in an important city like Jerusalem, the people would be sure to make Him king. They could take the opportunity to overthrow the Romans and reclaim Israel for themselves. They were happy to be a part of this—happy to have been chosen by God for such an important event.

"We will go on to Jerusalem," continued Jesus. Then He turned to face His disciples. "And there I must suffer many things. I will be rejected by the chief priests and the teachers of the law, and I will be killed."

Whatever joy the disciples had felt turned into utter shock. No one spoke. Eventually Judas managed a barely audible, "No."

"I will be killed," Jesus continued, "and on the third day, I will rise again."

The old prisoner scratched his beard.

"What Jesus said that day was confusing and heartbreaking for His disciples," he explained, "and it didn't stop there. Jesus continued to surprise everyone with ideas that were new and revolutionary! Like 'Love your enemies' and 'Do good to the people who hate you!'"

"Love your enemies?" Titus chuckled.

"Yes," replied the old man. "Even those who cause us harm."

Titus suddenly looked uncomfortable and glanced over at the commander who shifted in his seat.

"But that teaching was nothing compared to one particular day when Jesus said: 'I am the living bread, which came down from heaven. If anyone eats of this bread, he will live eternally. And the bread that I will give will be My body, which I will give for the life of the world.'"

"No one really understood what He meant, and soon many people began to turn away and reject Jesus," the old prisoner said. Then he leaned forward, and he looked sad. "Even one of the twelve disciples, tempted by the devil, tried to take matters into his own hands."

Outside the cave it thundered again, and the rain began to pour. †

JUDAS
Taken from Matthew 26:14-16, Mark 14:10-11, Luke 22:1-6

Judas went to the chief priests and the officers of the temple guard and discussed with them how he might betray Jesus. Luke 22:4

Darkness had settled on the usually busy city of Jerusalem as a cloaked figure made its way down the dim, narrow alleyways in the direction of the temple. Avoiding the occasional passerby by remaining hidden within the shadows, the figure finally arrived at the last street across from the open temple gate.

Carefully pulling the hood of his cloak over his eyes and lowering his head, he quickly ran across the street and into the temple.

There was little time to lose. The cloaked figure knew exactly where to go, having made previous arrangements for a meeting.

Across the courtyard, past a series of temple guards who seemed to recognize him, the cloaked man arrived at a long marble hallway, lit only by the oil lamps lining the walls. He stopped for a second, until his eyes adjusted and he could make out three black-cloaked figures, Pharisees, at the end of the hall. They motioned for him to approach.

The cloaked figure obeyed, and together the four began a discussion in very hushed tones. They whispered, they planned, and they plotted until they seemed to reach some sort of agreement.

"It is settled then?" asked the black-bearded Pharisee in a somber tone.

"Settled," replied the man in the cloak.

"Thirty pieces of silver," summarized the Pharisee.

"And I shall hand Jesus over to you," replied the cloaked man, "at the earliest opportunity." And he began his way back toward the entrance.

"Judas!" the Pharisee called out.

The cloaked man turned to the Pharisee.

"The sooner the better," said the Pharisee.

"Of course," replied Judas, and adjusting the hood of his cloak, he made his way to the door, hoping to return to Jesus and His disciples before he was missed. †

HOSANNA!

Taken from Matthew 21:1-11; Mark 11:1-11;
   Luke 19:28-44; John 12:12-19

*W*hen Jesus entered Jerusalem, the whole city was stirred and asked, "Who is this?" The crowds answered, "This is Jesus, the prophet from Nazareth in Galilee." Matthew 21:10-11

When the people of Jerusalem heard that Jesus and His disciples were approaching, the news and the excitement spread very rapidly. So much so that as soon as Jesus, sitting on a donkey, was visible outside the gates, the people ran out to welcome Him.

John and his companions had never seen anything like the greeting that followed.

Some of the people had cut down palm branches and placed them on the ground, creating a pathway into the city. Others took off their coats and added them to the improvised carpet Jesus and the donkey rode over. Still others waved palm branches over their heads as they danced.

Then the praises began, at first among the children; then picked up by the adults. The people cried out: "Blessed is He who comes in the name of the Lord! Hosanna! Hosanna! Praise to You!" It seemed like the whole city had come out to welcome Jesus.

A celebration worthy of a king, John thought to himself. And then he remembered the prophecy written in the book of Zechariah that said, *"Your king comes to you…riding on a donkey."*

Whatever concern or worry the disciples had over Jesus' announcement about coming to Jerusalem to be killed, vanished. Lost in the praise and festivity of the occasion, all thoughts of death were replaced with great happiness and satisfaction. The disciples loved Jesus, and were happy to see that others shared their love and respect for Him.

Among the joyful people, however, a group of men stood slightly apart, unhappy with the praise given to Jesus.

"This is getting seriously out of hand! We must do something!" the white-bearded Pharisee said as he looked on in disgust. Having witnessed as much as they could stand, the Pharisees turned and walked back to their chambers, leaving the cheering multitude behind. †

My Father's House

Taken from Matthew 21:12-14; Mark 11:15-17;
Luke 19:45-46; John 2:13-22

"It is written," he said to them, "'My house shall be called a house of prayer,' but you are making it a 'den of robbers.'" Matthew 21:13

While the joyous reception and exclamations of praise were still ringing in their ears, John, along with the other disciples, followed Jesus into the temple. Beaming with smiles, the disciples spoke among themselves about how much they could accomplish in Jerusalem, now that it was evident the people respected Jesus so much.

While they were still speaking to each other, John noticed Jesus had slowed down. Not only that, instead of going up toward the main buildings, Jesus had stopped to watch the animal vendors in the courtyard.

After a few moments, John followed Jesus as He walked among the vendors.

"That's outrageous!" an old man protested. "That dove isn't worth two shekels!"

"Fine!" replied the rude dove merchant. "No pay, no doves, no sacrifice—your choice! NEXT!"

Jesus walked farther, then stopped to hear a poor old woman arguing with another vendor.

"But I have brought my own doves for the sacrifice. I can't afford the ones you are trying to sell me," she explained.

"The only animals allowed for temple sacrifice are the ones sold here!" the merchant replied, not even bothering to look at the woman as he counted his coins.

"But why?" asked the old woman.

Losing his temper, the merchant pounded the table and leaped to his feet, causing the old woman nearly to lose her balance. "Because the Pharisees say so, that's why!" he yelled. "Now pay up or leave!"

John followed Jesus as He made His way around the monychangers, merchants, cages of doves and pens with lambs.

He listened to the endless haggling for money and better prices. Suddenly, he noticed Jesus had stopped walking. He just stood there, watching the constant business dealings, listening to the bleating of the sheep, the coos of the doves, the arguing, the sound of coins as they were dropping into full money chests.

John noticed that Jesus looked quite sad, almost heartbroken, as if someone had hurt Him very deeply. Wanting to comfort Him in some way, John was about to approach Jesus when he noticed the sorrow on Jesus' face was changing. Slowly His eyes narrowed, His eyebrows lowered, His lips became thin and tense, and His breathing became deep and shallow.

Curious as to what was happening, John barely had time to approach Jesus to ask, "Lord?" Before he knew what was happening, Jesus rushed right into the crowd of merchants, grabbed hold of an unsuspecting salesman's table and overturned it. Coins scattered everywhere. People hoping to avoid the table shoved back into other tables, tipping them over in the process. The merchant was stunned but hardly had time to react because Jesus was already at another table, overturning it as well before rushing to wipe another clear of coins and baskets. People screamed. Merchants chased their coins.

John didn't really know what to make of it. Soon, the other disciples were at his side, shocked as they watched Jesus free the caged doves and let the penned animals loose.

"Why?" Jesus bellowed, as He worked His way to another table and overturned it. "Why have you done this? Don't you know that this is My Father's house? But you…you have made it a den of thieves! Get out!" Jesus yelled.

The scene was chaotic with people trying to avoid Jesus, some of the merchants falling over each other or fighting among themselves for the scattered coins, while frightened animals ran loose. In the midst of this, the disciples stood back, not knowing what to say or what to do until….

"JESUS OF NAZARETH!" a voice roared above the ruckus.

John turned in the direction of the voice just in time to see the black-bearded Pharisee, followed by his companions, rushing into the courtyard.

Exhausted, Jesus turned to him.

"What is the meaning of this? WHAT?" the Pharisee spat out.

Jesus wasted no time in replying, and He did so loudly and boldly. "It is written: 'My temple shall be a house of prayer'…but you…." Jesus turned to all the merchants. "You have made it a den of thieves!" And He overturned another table.

"By what authority do You do this?" challenged the Pharisee. "BY WHAT?"

"Destroy this temple, and I will lift it up in three days!" Jesus replied.

"Ha! You're a madman!" sneered the Pharisee. "Forty-six years it took to build this temple and You…You will raise it up in three days?"

John could tell the Pharisees were confused by Jesus' reply. They had no idea that He was talking about the temple of His body and not the stone building in which they stood.

Without further word, Jesus turned and walked away. No sooner had He stepped out of the temple courtyard than He was surrounded once again by the blind and the sick. Jesus began to heal them all, as the angry Pharisees turned on their heels and headed back into their chambers.

There they would plot a way to get rid of Jesus.

The chief priests and the teachers of the law were looking for some way to get rid of Jesus, for they were afraid of the people. Luke 22:2

Not only were the Pharisees angry at the way Jesus rebuked them, but the fact that He had done so in public was more than they could bear. No sooner had Jesus and His followers left the temple grounds than the Pharisees got together to vent their fury and discuss how to get rid of Him and His followers; however, not all the Pharisees saw eye-to-eye on the matter.

"Outrageous! A threat to our authority!" one of the Pharisees raged. "We can't just stand by and let Jesus get away with that kind of behavior!"

"I agree!" chimed in another Pharisee. "Are we simply to stand by and let Him lead our people astray?"

"Worse than that" still another joined in, "He utterly humiliated us in public!"

"Yet," the gray-bearded Pharisee stood up and took the floor. "I find nothing in His teaching that contradicts ours."

"I agree," added another Pharisee. "His teaching is sound."

"WHAT?" the white-bearded Pharisee leaped to his feet. "You saw what happened today—tables overturned, coins scattered, animals running loose!"

"We must admit, however," replied the gray-bearded Pharisee, trying to calm everyone down, "that the selling of the animals was getting out of hand. People have been cheated, and some merchants treat it more as a business than a provision for the temple sacrifices. Jesus simply pointed that out in a very...well...in a very vivid way."

"But what will it lead to next?" shouted the black-bearded Pharisee. "Will Jesus stop at nothing to get a point across?"

Everyone began speaking at once, until Caiaphas, the high priest, broke through the commotion. "Have I heard correctly that He calls Himself the king of the Jews?"

"With your pardon, Caiaphas," replied the gray-bearded Pharisee. "The people have given Him that title—He did not claim it for Himself."

"And neither has He refused it," challenged Caiaphas.

"Which could make Him guilty of treason, and that could bring the wrath of the Romans upon us and upon our people!"

That thought had not yet occurred to the other Pharisees, and the mood became very somber.

"Consider another option then," Caiaphas continued. "Rather than lose an entire nation to the Roman's wrath, only one man should die."

There was stunned silence as the men thought about what Caiaphas was suggesting. Knowing Jesus was a good man, the gray-bearded Pharisee looked around nervously, hoping the matter would go no further than mere discussion. After a few moments, however, some of the Pharisees offered their opinions.

"I agree with you, Caiaphas!" the white-bearded Pharisee said.

"As do I!" agreed the black-bearded Pharisee. "If He is allowed to continue, Jesus of Nazareth will bring nothing but harm to our nation. We must get rid of Him."

While the majority of the Pharisees nodded their agreement, the gray-bearded Pharisee tried to think of some way to stop what seemed to be an unavoidable plan, but it was too late.

"Agreed. We will get rid of Jesus of Nazareth at the earliest opportunity," Caiaphas emphasized, while the majority of the Pharisees nodded their agreement. "How do you propose we go about it?"

The black-bearded Pharisee scratched his chin as he thought for a moment.

"Since the disturbance at the temple grounds, we do not know where He is," explained the Pharisee. Just then, however, he spied Judas making his way into the courtyard.

"But I believe we can trace His whereabouts." He smiled.

"Then see to it!" replied Caiaphas, and as he and the others stood to leave, the black-bearded Pharisee made his way to Judas, who would be instrumental in leading him to Jesus. †

THE LAST SUPPER

Taken from Matthew 26:17-30, Mark 14:12-31, John 13:1-34

"What you are about to do, do quickly." John 13:27

It was evening, just before the yearly Passover festival when all Jews celebrated their release from Egyptian slavery. Jesus and His disciples were gathered together in a second floor room where He had instructed them to prepare for their special evening meal.

Passover was always a very meaningful occasion, and the disciples were looking forward to an evening of rest from their labors, as well as from the crowds that usually followed them.

They were all seated at the table and the meal was being served, when Jesus stood, took a basin, and filled it with water. Then He wrapped a towel around His waist, and to the disciples' surprise and utter shock, Jesus knelt before them, unfastened their sandals, and began to wash their feet in the basin and to dry them with His towel.

John watched as each disciple shrank back uncomfortably when Jesus carefully washed away the dust and grime from their feet, pouring clean water over them.

This is a job for servants and slaves, not for an important person like Jesus! thought John. *Why is He humiliating Himself this way?*

Finally, Jesus knelt before Peter, but as He tried to dip his feet in the basin, Peter pulled them away.

"No, Lord!" Peter protested. "This job is for servants—not for You!" But Jesus took hold of his feet again and began to wash them.

"Peter," Jesus said, "you call Me Lord, and you are right in doing so because that is what I am. Now that I, your Lord and Teacher, have washed your feet, you also should wash one another's feet. I have set an example that you should do for each other, just as I have done for you."

Then standing up, Jesus picked up the basin and said, "Everyone will know that you are My disciples by the way you show love to one another."

The disciples would never forget this vivid and very real lesson. Jesus did not seek honor, but as He had told them many times before, He had come to serve.

Later that evening, after they had finished eating and singing a few hymns, Jesus sighed deeply, leaning His head against the wall.

John, who was sitting next to Jesus, whispered, "What is it, Lord?"

Jesus sighed again. "One of you will betray Me," He said sadly.

Those who sat closest to Jesus, who heard His words, went silent. Soon hushed whispers traveled among the disciples. "Who would do such a thing?" they asked each other.

Overcome with grief, John whispered to Jesus, "Lord, who is it? Who will betray You?"

"The one to whom I will give this bread," Jesus replied, as He took a small piece of bread, dipped it in His cup, and handed it to Judas.

John watched as Judas reached over for the bread.

"What you are about to do," Jesus said to Judas, "do quickly."

Something seemed to be happening to Judas. The first thing John noticed was that Judas stared right back at Jesus—defiantly. The look was chilling, but before John could take it all in, Judas leaped to his feet, never taking his eyes off Jesus. Then he quickly turned and went out the door.

"Where is he going?" some of the disciples whispered. *Perhaps to buy more food, or on some errand*, they thought to themselves.

But the disciples were wrong. No one could guess what Judas had really gone out to do. He wasn't getting more food or going on any errands.

In the dead of night, as everyone celebrated Passover, Judas was hurrying to the Pharisees to tell them where they could find Jesus and arrest Him. †

SORROW
Taken from Mathew 26:17-35, Mark 14:12-31, Luke 22:7-38

"This is my body given for you.... This cup is the new covenant in my blood, which is poured out for you." Luke 22:19-20

The hour was very late when John and the disciples finally left the upper room where they had celebrated the Passover, and stepped out into the cool, night air. The evening had begun in a festive and happy mood, but things had taken on a more serious tone. As he and the others followed Jesus into the courtyard, John thought about the evening's events and wondered: *Why had Judas left so suddenly, and where had he gone? Why did Jesus seem so very sad, and what had He meant by calling the wine and bread His body and His blood?*

"Take and eat," John recalled Jesus saying, as He took bread, blessed it and passed it around to the disciples. "This is My body, which is broken for you."

Each one had taken a piece of the bread and eaten it. Then Jesus had taken a cup of wine and said, "This is my blood, which will be poured out for many for the forgiveness of sins." He had passed the cup around, and each one of the disciples had taken a drink from it.

Though they did not really understand what He meant by calling the bread and wine His body and blood, they trusted Him. More importantly, they knew Jesus loved them, and this evening He had told them so repeatedly.

They now made their way into the courtyard, and John's happy memories were shaken when Jesus announced, "Tonight you all will abandon Me. As the scripture has said: 'I will strike the shepherd, and the sheep will be scattered.'"

John stopped walking immediately, as did most of the others. Suddenly he felt afraid.

"But after I rise, I will go ahead of you to Galilee," Jesus added.

"No!" Peter rushed to Jesus' side. He looked tormented and distressed. "Even if everyone else fails You, I never will, Lord! Never!"

Jesus lowered His gaze. "Peter," He said sadly. "Satan wants to test you, but I have already prayed for you— that your faith may not fail. And when all of this is over, Peter, strengthen your brothers!"

Peter was upset. "I assure You, I would do anything for You, Lord!" Placing his hand on Jesus' shoulder, he added, "I would even die for You if necessary!"

Jesus clasped Peter's hand. "Peter, not only will you deny Me, but before the rooster crows this morning, you will have done so three times."

Peter was stunned—speechless. Then unable to contain himself, he embraced Jesus tightly. "No, Lord!" he cried. "I will never deny You! Never!" And tears streamed down his cheeks. †

THE ARREST
Taken from Matthew 26:36-56, Mark 14:32-52, Luke 22:29-52, John 18:1-12

"My Father, if it is possible, may this cup be taken from me. Yet not as I will, but as you will." Matthew 26:39

On other occasions, Jesus had taken Peter, James and John to private places for a time of prayer. That is why John did not find it so unusual when Jesus asked them to accompany Him to one of His favorite places of prayer, the garden of Gethsemane.

The beauty of the abundant olive trees created sheltered areas perfect for quiet prayer and rest.

"Stay here and pray," Jesus had requested of the three as He went a little farther away to pray alone.

John had never seen Jesus quite so sad, and he wanted to please Him by praying as he had been asked. The hour was quite late, however, and the evening had been a strain on their emotions. Peter, James and John were tired.

The last thing John saw before dozing off to sleep was Jesus falling to His knees to pray. John had seen this before, but something was different about the way Jesus was praying. More than praying—Jesus appeared to be pleading, begging….

Overcome with tiredness, John closed his eyes and fell asleep.

Had John remained awake, he would indeed have seen Jesus praying in a way he had never seen before. Jesus was desperately pleading and begging His Father in heaven—so much so, He was sweating drops of blood.

"Father!" Jesus begged. "If it is possible…please take this cup from Me."

"Nevertheless," He added, "not My will, but Your will be done, Father!"

Twice Jesus had gone to wake the three disciples, asking them to stay awake and pray with Him. Each time they had fallen asleep. So Jesus continued to pray alone. He knew what He was about to face was very difficult, and He prayed that He might be spared from it; however, He always ended His prayer by repeating, "Not My will, but Your will be done."

When His time of prayer was finished, Jesus went back and woke His sleeping disciples.

"Lord?" John rubbed his eyes. He wanted to apologize for being too tired to pray, but Jesus spoke.

"The hour has come. He who betrays Me is here," Jesus said.

As John sat up, he could make out some flickering torches in the distance through the trees. By the time the large group of armed men and guards from the chief priest and Pharisees arrived, Peter and James had gotten to their feet and stood with John, behind Jesus.

The guards moved aside to make room as a cloaked figure walked through their midst and went straight to Jesus.

"Rabbi," said Judas, as he greeted Jesus with a kiss on the cheek.

"Judas, do you betray Me with a kiss?" replied Jesus.

Turning His gaze to the guards, Jesus asked, "Who are you seeking?"

"Jesus of Nazareth," came the reply from the head guard.

"I am He," Jesus stated. "Am I a robber that you come with swords and clubs to take Me by force? I taught daily in the temple, and you didn't take Me then. But I know the scriptures must be fulfilled."

"Take Him!" yelled the guard, and his companions closed in on Jesus, grabbing Him while one tried to bind Him with heavy chains. Judas, fearing what could happen, stepped away into the darkness of the woods.

"Leave Him alone!" John cried out, while James did his best to push some of the guards to the side, causing them to fall over. Seeing his chance, Peter rushed to Jesus, hoping to pull Him away from the soldiers. But he was blocked by a guard, while another grabbed him from behind and put a sword to his throat.

Not willing to give up, Peter twisted the soldier to the ground, took his sword and ran to help Jesus. As the servant of the High Priest lunged to stop him, Peter struck him with his sword.

"Auuughhhh!" the servant screamed in pain as his severed ear fell to the ground.

At this, several guards pounced on Peter, trying to take the sword from him. But Peter continued to swing the sword wildly.

"Peter!" Jesus shouted. "Put your sword away!"

Surprised by Jesus' command, Peter stopped and was quickly captured; yet he clung to the sword. John could tell Peter agonized over obeying what Jesus was telling him to do. Peter wanted nothing more than to free his Lord, the one he loved—yet Jesus Himself was prohibiting him.

John could see the tears well up in Peter's eyes as Jesus said, "Don't you know that I can pray to My Father and He will provide Me with more than twelve legions of angels to protect Me?"

Peter dropped the sword. Sensing Jesus wanted no fight, the soldiers loosened their grasp on Him. Jesus immediately fell to His knees in front of Malchus, the servant whose ear Peter had cut off. He picked up the severed ear and placed it on the servant's bloodied wound.

"Be healed," Jesus commanded. And Malchus slowly calmed down.

"Let's go!" called out the main guard, as they grabbed Jesus and took Him away.

Peter remained on the ground, sobbing, calling out his Lord's name, as John and James tried to comfort him. Malchus, standing with one hand cupped over his ear, watched as Jesus was taken away—stunned to realize his ear was completely healed. †

" *A* re you then the Son of God?" Luke 22:70

Out of breath and keeping to the darkness so they wouldn't be recognized, John and Peter stumbled into the outer wall of the high priest's house where Jesus had just been taken.

"Wait here! Maybe I can find out what is happening," whispered John.

And before Peter could stop him, John made his way into the courtyard toward the entrance of the house.

Not wishing to remain alone, Peter gathered enough courage to at least enter the courtyard, making sure his face was well-hidden under his cloak.

The courtyard was full of temple guards, house servants and the curious. News of Jesus' arrest had traveled quickly, and some of the Pharisees were streaming into the building, preparing for a council.

Looking around, Peter made his way to a fire where only a few people sat. Cautiously staying apart from the crowd, he found a place near corner of the wall and sat down, keeping his face lowered.

Inside the house, John made his way past groups of people arguing heatedly, some saying it was high time the Pharisees had taken action against Jesus and His false claims, while others argued that Jesus was a good man. The tension in the room was high, and John found a place behind a pillar, away from the mob, where he could get a better view of the events. Standing behind a lattice, he could see the High Priest, the Pharisees, some soldiers, an angry mob and—to his utter horror—what they had done to Jesus.

What he saw made him gasp, and he grabbed on to a pillar for support to keep himself under control. The knuckles of his hands turned white at the strain. He gasped for breath, and then tears flowed.

Jesus stood in front of the High Priest, heavy chains around His neck connecting to shackles on both His wrists and feet. The chains were obviously too short, causing Him to stand slightly bent over. His robe was torn, His hair stringy with dry blood and His face—His face made John want to look away. Jesus had gashes with blood seeping from them; one of his eyes was purple-black and nearly swollen shut. Another bloody gash was over His cheekbone, and His lips were bloodied and swollen. He stood silent.

"You have nothing to say against these accusations?" bellowed Caiaphas, the High Priest.

But to everyone's astonishment, Jesus kept silent.

"Answer the High Priest when he is talking to You!" shouted the black-bearded Pharisee.

"I have spoken openly in both the synagogues and the temple and have said nothing in secret. Why don't you ask those who have heard Me?" Jesus replied.

No sooner had He answered than one of the guards slapped Jesus across the mouth, sending Him to the floor.

"You dare speak to the High Priest that way?" the guard shouted, as he pulled Jesus back up by His hair.

"If I have spoken any evil, tell Me!" Jesus managed to say. "But if not, why do you hit Me?"

Enraged by Jesus' reply, the soldier raised his fist to strike once more.

"Stop!" the High Priest ordered. The soldier backed away, but not before spitting on Jesus' face, humiliating Him even more.

"Let us get to the heart of the matter," continued Caiaphas as he approached Jesus. "There are many people here who have brought serious accusations against You. In fact, they say that You—a mere man—dare to say You are...." The High Priest could hardly bear to say the words, and he hesitated for a moment. "They say You claim to be the...Son of God."

At this, the mob inside the room broke out into loud accusations and shouts of "Blasphemy!" Had it not been for the guards, the mob would have pounced on Jesus in a fury.

Raising his hand, Caiaphas brought some order to the room, and the people once again calmed down as the guards regained control.

"Tell us plainly," Caiaphas circled around Jesus. "Are You the Christ, the Son of the living God?"

The room grew silent.

Jesus raised His head and replied, "I am."

What happened next was nothing short of a frenzied explosion of rage. Those nearest to Jesus leaned in as far as they could past the guards, striking Him with their fists, slapping Him, spitting at Him, or throwing their sandals if that's all they could manage to do.

In the midst of this chaos, Jesus' voice rose above the madness and noise, "And hereafter," He said loudly, "you will see Me sitting at the right hand of God and coming with the clouds of heaven!"

Hearing Jesus' statement, the crowd became furious. The High Priest, trembling with rage, took hold of his outer cloak, and tore his robe in two—a gesture of the greatest disapproval, which sent gasps across the room.

"We need no more witnesses!" Caiaphas roared. "What is your judgement?" he asked the mob.

The reply came swiftly: "Death! Put Jesus to death!"

Eager to consent, Caiaphas motioned for Jesus to be taken away as the mob cheered. Only one man remained sorrowful and weeping. John held on to a pillar for strength, in shock at the turn of events. Only a week before, Jesus was being praised as the Messiah.

As Jesus was being hauled away, John stumbled toward the corridor and hurriedly followed the crowd to the door.

Outside, Peter warmed himself by the fire, doing his best to hide his identity from people who had gathered to talk and argue about the night's events. When the mob emerged from the house with Jesus, Peter looked up and soon caught the eye of a woman who sat nearby.

"Wait a minute," she grabbed his cloak and pulled it off his face. "I've seen you! You're one of His followers, aren't you?" She pointed to Jesus who was now being brought through the courtyard.

"No," Peter was quick to reply. "I don't know Him. I…I don't know what you are talking about!"

"Yes, you do!" the woman insisted. "I saw you with Him. I'm sure of it!"

"NO! You've…you've got the wrong man," Peter insisted nervously, as he stood to go.

"She's right!" a servant who had turned at the woman's remark, now blocked Peter's way. "You're a Galilean! A follower of Jesus! I saw you in the garden with…."

Peter pushed the man away. "I tell you I don't know the man! I swear!"

Somewhere a rooster was crowing.

Jesus' words came back to him: "Before the rooster crows this morning, you will have denied Me three times."

Overcome with fear and shame, Peter ran into the shadows and wept. †

"*I* have betrayed innocent blood." Matthew 27:4

With the mob gone and Jesus arrested, a few of the Pharisees remained in discussion with Caiaphas.

"The laws of Moses state it plainly: Jesus' blasphemy is worthy of death," the black-bearded Pharisee said.

"But how can we carry out that punishment?" the white-bearded Pharisee questioned. "Roman law strictly prohibits us from putting anyone to death."

"We may be prohibited," interrupted Caiaphas, "but the Romans are not. They can see to His execution." Then turning to leave, he added, "Take Jesus to the Roman governor. He'll know what to do."

The remaining Pharisees nodded and smiled. It made perfect sense to turn Jesus over to the Romans.

Two guards, who had caught up with a man trying to make his way to the Pharisees, interrupted their discussion. Recognizing Judas, one of the Pharisees motioned the guards to let him through.

Judas, looking quite upset and nervous, rushed to them. "I have betrayed innocent blood!" he lamented.

The black-bearded Pharisee simply shrugged his shoulders and said, "And what is that to us? We had an agreement, and we have kept our part of the bargain. Take the money and go!"

"No!" Judas persisted. "I don't want it anymore! Take it back! Take all of it!"

Then throwing the 30 pieces of silver at their feet, he staggered toward the door, mumbling to himself as he went, "I have betrayed Him! I have betrayed an innocent man!"

A few hours later, the sun was rising on a field at the outskirts of Jerusalem—a field where a lone tree stood. There beneath one of the branches hung the body of Judas Iscariot. He had hung himself, ending his life by his own hand. †

Then Pilate took Jesus and had him flogged. John 19:1

Early in the morning, after a further beating by the temple guards, Jesus was taken to Pontius Pilate, the Roman governor.

"This man is a criminal!" the Pharisees and the elders of the people shouted.

"So why do you bring Him to me? You have your laws—why don't you judge Him?" Pilate replied.

"Because the law does not allow us to put anyone to death!" replied the Pharisees.

So insistent were the Pharisees that Jesus should be condemned to death, Pilate decided to question Jesus himself.

"What have You done that Your own people want to put You to death?" Pilate questioned Jesus.

"My kingdom isn't from this world," Jesus replied. "If it were, My servants would fight to free Me."

"Ah, so You consider Yourself a king!" Pilate concluded.

"You say I am," replied Jesus. "I was born for one purpose: to give testimony to the truth. Anyone who hungers for the truth, will hear My voice."

The time spent with Jesus was intriguing for Pilate yet he could find nothing in Jesus' replies that deserved death. Going back to where the Pharisees had assembled, he informed them: "I have questioned the man, and I cannot find any fault in Him," Pilate announced.

But the Jews would not accept his conclusion and cried out all the more for Jesus to be put to death!

Attempting to appease them, Pilate called over a soldier. "Take this man," he commanded regarding Jesus, "and have Him flogged!"

The Roman soldier did as he was told and Jesus was taken to another part of the governor's palace where He was tied to a post and whipped by several soldiers.

Binding His hands to a pillar, the soldiers stripped Jesus of His clothes, while nearby two soldiers waited, each with a whip in his hand—a whip made of nine leather strands with pieces of bone and lead on the end.

"So this is the one they call the king of the Jews!" sneered one of the soldiers, eyeing Jesus up and down. "Well then, we'll just have to give You the royal treatment!" he laughed.

Once Jesus was secured to the pillar, the two soldiers positioned themselves behind Him.

"How many lashes?" one of the soldiers asked the captain.

"Thirty-nine," came the reply as the captain sat on a stool to supervise.

"Alright," said one of the two soldiers as they both tightened their grip around the whip handles. "Ready for the count."

The captain raised his hand in preparation for the signal.

Jesus, exhausted from the night's events, leaned into the pillar and closed His eyes.

"One!" shouted the captain. The whip sang through the air and wrapped around Jesus. Just as quickly, the soldier pulled the strands away, tearing the flesh on His back.

Jesus screamed.

"Two!" the captain called out. A whip struck Jesus from the opposite side, crisscrossing the first gashes. Jesus gasped; His eyes wide.

"Three!" continued the captain and again the whip fell hard on Jesus' back.

More screams—blood splattered on the ground, the pillar, even on the soldiers themselves.

"Four! Five! Six...!" On and on the captain called out the numbers as the bones and lead pounded Jesus' back, arms and legs. His body, a bloody and torn mess, Jesus hung limp from the pillar, His legs having buckled under His weight.

Somewhere in the middle of the punishment, when the whipping soldiers needed to catch their breath, Jesus was turned so the front of his body, yet untouched by the whips, could receive the rest of His punishment.

"Let's get on with it!' ordered the captain. The whipping continued; Jesus writhed in pain with each blow; His body trembling from the shock; His voice too weak to scream anymore.

"Thirty-nine!" The last lash came down hard and the soldiers, wiping the sweat from their blood-sprinkled brows, sat down to rest and have some water. They did not have long to rest, however; just then, another soldier marched in.

"Bring Him!" he ordered. "Pilate wants Him now."

The two tired soldiers made their way to Jesus, laughing at His condition. "He got the royal treatment alright," one of them chuckled as they helped Him to His feet and pushed Him toward the gate.

"Wait!" The captain of the soldiers came forward, holding a twisted mesh of long thorny branches. "Let's not forget the king's crown!" he mocked as he forced the thorny crown on Jesus' head, causing trickles of blood to flow down His face.

"Wait just a moment! A king without a robe is not a king at all!" joked another soldier as he picked up a purple robe and threw it over Jesus' shoulders.

The soldiers roared with laughter as they bowed before Jesus and shouted, "Hail the king of the Jews! Hail!" †

CRUCIFY HIM!

Taken from Matthew 27:11-26, Mark 15:1-15,
Luke 23:1-24, John 19:1-16

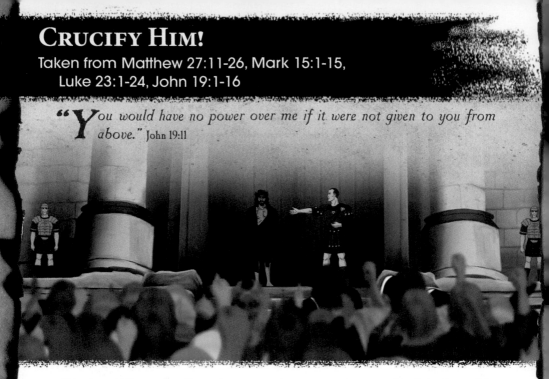

"*You would have no power over me if it were not given to you from above.*" John 19:11

Pontius Pilate, the Roman governor, stepped onto the large marble terrace as the people shouted out demands, pleadings and accusations, all having to do with Jesus. In the very front of the crowd, where they could be closest to Pilate, stood the Pharisees.

Raising his hand to quiet the people, Pilate spoke:

"You brought me a man that you say has broken the law. I questioned Him and found Him guilty of no crime! But you insisted on punishment, and therefore, He has been punished!" Motioning to his right, Pilate added, "Behold, the man!"

No one was prepared for the sight that followed. All eyes focused on the trembling figure of a man, drenched head to foot in blood and covered with gashes. He was draped in a purple robe and wore a crown of long, sharp thorns.

The black-bearded Pharisee pointed to Jesus and shouted, "Blasphemer! Blasphemer!" His companions picked up the cry, while rallying the people around them to join in.

Pilate approached Jesus, asking privately, "What have You done to make these people hate You so?" But Jesus remained silent.

Pilate thought for a moment and then, motioning a soldier to approach, he whispered a command. As the soldier quickly exited, Pilate once again addressed the crowd.

"We have a custom to free one prisoner during your festive days," he announced. "What do you say? Shall I deliver Jesus, who is called the Christ, to you or…Barabbas?"

As Pilate motioned them forward, two soldiers escorted a wild-looking man—well-known among the people for his crimes.

Some people in the crowd began to spread the word: "The Pharisees want you to call out for Barabbas! Ask for Barabbas!"

"Which of these two do you want me to release to you?" repeated Pilate.

"Barabbas!" the people shouted. "Free Barabbas!"

"And what of this man?" asked Pilate. "What then shall I do with this Jesus, who is called the Christ?"

Seizing the opportunity to get rid of Jesus, the black-bearded Pharisee yelled out, "Put Him to death! Crucify Him!"

"But why? What evil has He done?" questioned Pilate.

"We have a law," responded a Pharisee. "And according to that law, He must die because He claimed to be the Son of God!"

Hearing this, the crowd went into a fury with some people yelling, "Take Him away! Take Him away! Crucify Him!"

Shocked by the hatred the crowd showed for Jesus, Pilate approached Him again. "Explain to me: Who are You? Where do You come from?" he asked.

Jesus said nothing.

"Do You refuse to answer me? Don't You realize I have power to free You or crucify You?" Pilate threatened.

Jesus turned to him and replied, "You would have no power over Me if it were not given to you from above. Therefore the one who handed Me over to you is guilty of the greater sin."

Pilate was torn between what he felt was the unjust treatment of an innocent man and the demands of the bloodthirsty crowd.

Turning back to the people, Pilate said, "I tell you, I find no fault in Him!"

"He calls Himself a king!" shouted a Pharisee.

"And?" questioned Pilate.

"We have no king but Caesar!" challenged the Pharisee. "And you know good and well that acknowledging Jesus as king is nothing more than treason!"

Treason was punishable by death. Now Pilate had no choice but to sentence Jesus to death.

Even then, Pilate was hesitant to pass such a severe judgment on Jesus, but he had little choice.

Motioning a servant to bring a basin of water, Pilate washed his hands and declared: "Then let the record show that I am innocent of this man's death, for I find no fault in Him. I am innocent of the blood of this just person!"

As he stepped back into his palace, Pilate turned to the Pharisee and added, "You see to His death!"

The Pharisee replied, "His blood be upon us, and on our children."

The crowd cheered in agreement, and as Barabbas was set free, Jesus was led away. †

"*Surely this man was the Son of God!*" Mark 15:39

When news spread that Jesus was going to be put to death, people gathered outside the palace entrance and lined the streets nearly all the way to the hill where the public execution would take place.

As the gates to the palace opened, a group of armed Roman soldiers stepped out, pushing the rowdy people to the side. Those closest to the gates strained to get a look at Jesus, who slowly staggered onto the street, stumbling under the weight of the large wooden cross He carried on His back.

Behind Him two other men followed—thieves who had also been sentenced to die—but they carried no full crosses on their shoulders as Jesus did, only the crosspiece to which their hands were tied.

Having alerted Jesus' mother of her Son's fate, John now did his best to guide Mary through the crowds. But it was nearly impossible, partly because of the large number of people lining the streets and partly because the soldiers pushed them back. Sometimes, all they could see was the top of the cross making its way forward.

Mary wept openly, her heart breaking every time she heard insults heaped upon Jesus—every time she heard the soldiers cursing Him—every time she heard the whip rip through the air to lash her Son's skin when He fell, as He had just now.

Jesus lay on the ground, having collapsed under the weight of the cross. Realizing they would have to help Him, the soldiers grabbed an unsuspecting man from the crowd and forced him to carry Jesus' cross. Slowly Jesus got back on His feet and continued down the route leading to a place just outside the city walls called "The Skull," where He would be put to death.

Once Jesus had made the long and agonizing trek, the Romans wasted no time. Taking the cross off His back, they stripped Jesus of His purple robe, parts of which had stuck to His open wounds.

Leaving Him with nothing more than a cloth wrapped around His waist, they laid Jesus on the cross and placed each of His hands over the extreme parts of the horizontal beams.

John and Mary, and a few other sympathetic women stood nearby. John could feel Mary's grip tightening around his hand in anticipation of what was to follow. None of them spoke.

One of the soldiers placed a long, rugged nail in one of Jesus' hands, partly piercing the skin. Then he grabbed a heavy, wooden mallet, lifted it high above his head and swung it down in full force on the nail.

Jesus screamed.

Mary fell to her knees, and John did his best to break her fall. The other women hid their faces and shrieked.

Having hammered Jesus' hand to one beam, the soldier made his way to the other hand. By the time John turned to see what was happening, the mallet was striking the nail.

Jesus writhed in pain, His weak body trembling as blood flowed from both hands into the wood and dropped to the ground.

Mary shook and paled as she looked up at her Son, tears pouring down her face.

Jesus moaned.

The soldiers grabbed Jesus' feet and extended his legs along the vertical beam. Placing His feet one atop the other, one of the soldiers held them still while a much longer and larger nail was positioned on top of them. The mallet came down, and the nail pierced straight through both feet, clamping Jesus entirely to the cross.

Again Jesus screamed, and His body shook uncontrollably from the shock.

Tears rolled down John's face, and the women wept loudly.

The soldiers hoisted the cross so that it stood upright, causing Jesus terrible pain.

"Father, forgive them!" Jesus prayed as He hung on the cross. "They don't know what they are doing!"

The two thieves who had accompanied Him through the streets, having also been crucified, were placed on either side of Jesus.

Once all three crosses were in position, Pilate ordered a sign fastened to the top of Jesus' cross, which read "Jesus of Nazareth, the King of the Jews." When the Pharisees read it they became angry and complained to Pilate saying, "Do not write that He is the King of the Jews but rather that He claimed to be that!"

But to their dismay, Pilate simply answered, "What I have written, I have written!"

Being that she was Jesus' mother, Mary and her companions were allowed to approach. She knelt in front of the cross, clutching her heart and weeping as she looked upon her Son, hanging on the cross.

Three hours had passed since Jesus had been placed on the cross, and the only people that remained at the crucifixion site were John, Mary and the other women. The Roman soldiers, who had made a sport of the day by gambling to see who among them got to keep Jesus' purple robe, remained to guard the cross.

"Look at Him!" mocked the black-bearded Pharisee who along with his companions had come to witness what they had wanted for so long.

"He saved other people and yet He cannot even save Himself! Let Him come down from the cross, and then we will believe Him!"

The thought made his companion laugh, and he added, "Let God rescue Him; after all, didn't He say He was God's Son?"

Laughing among themselves, the Pharisees turned and walked away, but not before the black-bearded Pharisee caught a glimpse of Mary, who sat nearby with John, her tear-stained face gazing intently at her Son.

For a moment, he simply stared at her. His smile disappeared; then he lowered his gaze, turned and along with the other Pharisees, made his way in the direction of the city and their temple.

One of the crucified thieves turned to Jesus. "I thought You were the Christ," he groaned. Then he added with an accusatory yell, "Why don't You save Yourself and us?"

"Quiet!" the other thief yelled out. "Don't you have any fear of God?" Then lowering his head, he added, "We're criminals—we deserve this. But this man...this man has done nothing wrong."

Then turning to Jesus, he added, "Jesus, remember me when You enter Your kingdom."

Slowly and with some difficulty, Jesus turned to look at him. "Today you will be with Me in paradise," He said.

Then looking down toward His mother, Jesus called her.

John helped Mary get closer to the cross where they stood looking helplessly at Jesus.

"Mother," Jesus continued. "This is your son." And He looked over at John adding, "This is your mother."

John nodded. He understood. Jesus knew He would not be with them much longer, and He was asking John to care for His mother.

By then, it was nearly noon, and the sky began to darken.

Near three o'clock, thick, black clouds had gathered. Mary, John and the others had not left Jesus' side. He had been on the cross now for nearly six agonizing hours.

Slowly and with some difficulty, Jesus lifted up His head and looked at the sky, now dark with gray clouds. "Father!" He cried. "Father, why have You abandoned Me?"

Mary wept.

The wind blew and the sky grew even darker.

"It is finished," Jesus whispered. And looking up once again He prayed, "Father, into Your hands I commit My spirit."

His head tilted back for a moment and then dropped to one side.

Jesus died.

For a moment, only the sound of the wind and the whimpering of the women could be heard. Then an earthquake shook the ground, accompanied by a loud thundering from the sky.

At the temple, the Pharisees panicked as walls tumbled and burning oil lamps fell to the ground. It was all they could do to stay on their feet, and some of them stumbled downstairs, the black-bearded Pharisee among them.

He stopped near the most important section of the temple—the Holy of Holies. It was the room that housed the Ark of the Covenant—a representation of God's presence—behind a thick curtain 60 feet high, 30 feet wide and four inches thick. To his horror the curtain ripped down the middle, from top to bottom, as if powerful, invisible hands were tearing it apart.

"No!" yelled the Pharisee in horror. "NO!"

On the hill outside the city where Jesus' body hung on the cross, confused and scared soldiers picked themselves up off the ground. One of them approached John and Mary, their eyes still fixed on Jesus.

Shaking in fear the soldier took off his helmet and exclaimed, "Surely this man was the Son of God."

The next day was the Sabbath, and Jewish religion did not allow people to work on that day. Because of this, the Pharisees asked the Roman soldiers to make sure all three victims were dead. The two thieves were still alive, so the Romans broke their legs to make their death quicker. When they came to Jesus, they realized He was already dead, so rather than break His legs, they took a spear and pierced His side.

This was a fulfillment of two ancient prophecies: "Not one of His bones will be broken," and "They will look at the one they have pierced."

Finishing their job, the Roman soldiers made their way back to the city, leaving John, Mary and their companions to mourn the death of their Lord. †

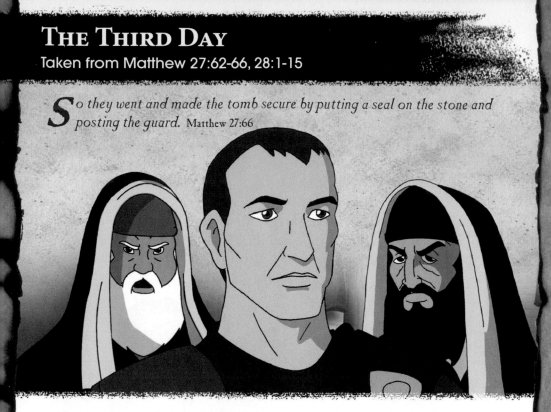

So they went and made the tomb secure by putting a seal on the stone and posting the guard. Matthew 27:66

The darkness of night had fallen over Jerusalem, and Jesus had been dead for hours—buried in the tomb of Joseph of Arimathea, a man who generously offered his own burial plot.

The Pharisees should have been content with the day's outcome; they had gotten what they wanted, having rid themselves of Jesus. Yet they had one more concern, one more thing to take care of, and several of them had come to discuss it with Pilate.

"When Jesus was alive He told His followers that after three days He would rise from the dead," explained the black-bearded Pharisee. "In order to avoid any deception, send soldiers to guard the tomb. Then put your seal on the stone in front of the opening so it cannot be moved."

"That way," added the other Pharisee, "Jesus' followers can't steal the body and then tell people He rose from the dead."

"Fine," replied Pilate, eager to put an end to the whole matter. "I will do just as you have suggested. Let's hope this settles things once and for all."

Just before sunrise, on the outskirts of Jerusalem, a Roman soldier was trying to warm himself by a small fire while his fellow soldier paced back and forth impatiently. They had been guarding Jesus' tomb, which was sealed by a large, heavy stone.

"Three days guarding this tomb!" complained the impatient soldier. "Three days!"

"So you keep reminding me," replied the other wearily, as he added more wood to the fire.

"We don't have to guard all these other dead people…but this one—this one we have to guard!" continued the pacing soldier. "This is ridiculous! The man is dead, and no one rises from the dead!"

"Which is why we're here, remember?" replied the other soldier, as he continued to stoke the fire. "So none of Jesus' followers can steal the body and claim that He rose from the grave! Now quit complaining!" Then turning to glance at the sun rising over the horizon, he added, "Ah, good! It's been a cold night—warmth at last!"

But the impatient soldier wasn't finished complaining. After all, how important was it to guard a tomb? He should be with his fellow soldiers doing something more useful, like patrolling the city or guarding Pilate, instead of guarding some dead man. It was humiliating.

Leaning on the tomb, he continued to grumble, "Rise from the dead! What a ridiculu…."

The earth shook. It was a quick jolt, but strong enough that the next thing he knew, the grumbling soldier was facedown on the ground.

"What hap…?" he asked but he never finished his sentence for precisely at that moment another tremor was felt and the soldier and his companion turned just in time to see an angel appear next to the stone that sealed the tomb. With wings magnificently spread, the angel leaned heavily upon the stone, slowly pushing it away.

The earthquake, and the sight of the brilliantly shining angel were too much for the soldiers to handle. One and then the other collapsed from sheer fright, falling to the ground like dead men.

The angel continued with his task, rolling the stone completely away from the entrance of the tomb and letting it drop with a mighty thud to one side, causing a small cloud of dust to settle on the soldiers. It was probably better that they had fainted, for if they had been shocked by the sight of the angel, they may have died of fright at what happened next.

Instead of a dark tomb, the place where Jesus' body lay began to fill with light. But this was not sunlight streaming in from the outside. It was a light emanating from inside the tomb—light that was coming from the shrouded body itself.

Slowly, the light shone from within the shroud, reflecting off the stone-hewn cavern until in one burst of brilliance, the entire tomb filled with a glow and suddenly, Jesus sat up, opened His eyes, and smiled. †

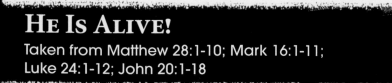

> "**G**o...to my brothers and tell them, 'I am returning to my Father and your Father, to my God and your God.'" John 20:17

The oil lamps that hung from the ceiling swung back and forth after the tremor, causing John and a few other disciples to leap to their feet.

"What was that?" John asked.

"An earthquake, a tremor...I don't know," Peter replied wearily.

Afraid of being arrested, the eleven remaining disciples had scattered after Jesus' death three days before. Slowly, all except Thomas had regrouped in one house where they kept the windows closed and the door bolted.

The present situation was a great contrast to the welcome they had enjoyed a week before when the people of Jerusalem received them with singing, praises and palm leaves.

Now, their leader had been accused of treason, tortured and killed, and they were in fear for their lives. Adding to the gloomy situation, many of the disciples felt ashamed and angry with themselves for deserting Jesus in His hour of suffering. Peter, in particular, was greatly ashamed; he had not only run away, but had denied even knowing Jesus. The guilt he felt seemed unbearable.

"You didn't sleep again, did you, Peter?" John asked. "You need sleep."

"I need peace, that's what I need," Peter sighed. Then repeating what he had been saying for days, he added, "I denied Him, John! I failed Jesus!"

"We were all afraid, Peter," John tried to comfort him.

"I just wish I could tell Him how ashamed I am," replied Peter. "I wish I could…."

There came a loud knock on the door. No one moved.

The knock came again—this time stronger and more insistent. James signaled for everyone to remain quiet.

The knock at the door now turned to pounding.

"I thought you said no one knew we were here!" Andrew whispered to James.

"They don't!" James replied in a low voice.

The pounding continued and before anyone could stop him, James went to the door. No sooner had he unbolted it than he was pushed aside as a woman rushed in.

Mary Magdalene, trying to catch her breath, seemed agitated and excited. "I saw Him!" she gasped.

"Saw who? What are you talking about?" Peter asked, getting to his feet.

"The Lord," Mary replied, motioning them to come closer. "Peter, John…all of you! Listen to me! He has risen, just as He said He would. Jesus has risen from the dead!" †

MY LORD AND MY GOD!

Taken from John 20:26-31, 21:15-23

"*Put your finger here; see my hands. Reach out your hand and put it into my side. Stop doubting and believe.*" John 20:27

Thomas couldn't believe it. *My friends must be going crazy*, he thought.

Having made his way to the room where the rest of his companions were hiding, Thomas just couldn't bring himself to believe what John and the others were telling him. They said Mary Magdalene had shared the news that Jesus had risen from the dead. At first, they too thought she was speaking nonsense—that is, until Jesus Himself had appeared to them.

"Thomas, listen to me," John begged. "We not only saw Jesus, we actually spoke with Him! Why do you think we would make this up?"

"Well, I just can't believe it, that's all!" Thomas was doubtful. "Unless I can put my finger on the place where the nails went through His hands, and put my hand in the wound where the spear pierced His side, I will not believe! I just…."

"Peace be unto you," a voice interrupted Thomas.

The voice was familiar—one that brought memories flooding to Thomas' mind, and a smile to the other disciples' faces. The voice came from behind him, and Thomas was hesitant to turn around—but he did so, rather slowly, until he found himself face to face with Jesus.

Thomas was speechless.

Jesus opened His hands and held them out. "Reach with your finger, Thomas, and touch My hands," He said.

Shaking at the sight before him, Thomas could clearly see the wounds Jesus still bore in His hands.

"And now," Jesus continued as He opened His robe, revealing a wound on the side of His chest, "reach out your hand and put it into My side."

By now Thomas was shaking from head to foot, and tears were streaming down his face. He looked into Jesus' eyes.

"Don't be faithless, Thomas," Jesus said, "but believe!"

Thomas fell to his knees, bowed his face to the ground, and cried out, "My Lord…and my God!"

Jesus smiled. Placing a hand on Thomas' shoulder, He said, "Thomas, because you have seen Me, you believe. Blessed are they who have not seen, yet they believe."

Throughout the next few days, Jesus continued to instruct His disciples, preparing them for the time He would return to His Father in heaven and they would carry on His mission.

John loved these visits with his Lord. He had been close to Jesus ever since the Baptist pointed Him out as the Lamb of God, Who had come to take away the sins of the world. He had spent three years in the company of Jesus, following Him as a disciple. At first, there were many things John had not understood. But now he knew God had loved the world so much He had sent His Son to be the Lamb of God—to take away the sins of the world—so anyone who believed in Jesus would have eternal life.

Jesus had given His life as payment for everyone's sins. The more John thought about that the more his heart burst with love for Jesus; he wanted to follow Him for the rest of his life.

And so on one occasion, when Jesus took Peter on a walk, John could not bear to be left behind, and he followed them at a distance. He couldn't make out what they were saying, but he was happy for Peter, who had suffered so long because he had denied Jesus three times.

As John followed, Jesus and Peter continued their conversation.

"Peter, do you love Me?" Jesus asked as they walked.

"Lord, this is the third time You have asked me. You know all things. You know I love You," Peter replied.

Jesus stopped walking and turning to Peter, He said, "Feed My sheep."

Peter nodded. Jesus had forgiven him for his weakness and had encouraged his faith. Peter was determined to do the same for others. He remembered what Jesus had said to him before, "When you are strengthened, Peter—strengthen your brothers."

Placing His hands on Peter's shoulders, Jesus said, "Peter, when you were a younger man you did just as you pleased and went wherever you wanted to go. But now, God is the one Who will take control and lead you. Sometimes He will lead you to places you never wanted to go. Will you go, Peter? Will you go to those places for Me even if it's dangerous?"

"Yes, Lord," Peter replied. "I will go wherever You ask me to; I will follow with all my heart."

As they continued to walk, Peter looked back and noticed John was following them.

"What about John, Lord?" Peter asked. "What do You want him to do?"

"Don't worry about John," Jesus replied. "If it is My will that he live until I return, what does it matter to you? You must follow Me, Peter. Just follow Me."

Jesus and Peter continued to walk along the shore, and John continued to follow them, happy just knowing Jesus was with them once again. ✝

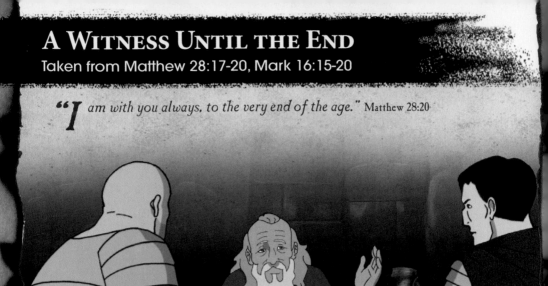

"*I am with you always, to the very end of the age.*" Matthew 28:20

The rain had stopped, and sunlight filtered into the cave where the old prisoner's story had kept his guards captivated.

"If it is My will that he live until I get back, what is that to you?" the old prisoner quoted with a faraway look.

"That's what Jesus said of John, His youngest disciple. So it was commonly thought he would not die, or put another way, he would not die at the hand of his enemies."

The old man looked straight at his guards. "And so far his enemies have caused him no harm," he said with a smile.

It took a moment for the two guards to understand what the old prisoner was implying.

"You?" Titus asked. "You're John?"

"The one the Empire has not been able to kill," added the commander.

"The others all died a martyr's death," continued John. "They all took the message of Jesus to the surrounding countries even though it cost their lives. I alone of the twelve remain, a witness to all Jesus said and did—a witness to the miracles, His love and to His parting message."

"What do you mean?" asked the commander. "Where did Jesus go?"

"The last day we spent with Him, He gathered us around and said, 'Go into all the world and preach the good news to every creature and make disciples of every nation. Teach them to obey everything I have taught you. And do not forget, I will be with you always, even unto the very end of the world.' And then, before our very eyes, Jesus was taken up into heaven."

The guards were silent. John had told them an amazing story, but they could tell he was not crazy. He had recounted what he had experienced—nothing more and nothing less.

"So you see," continued John, "how can I deny what I have seen with my own eyes and what I know to be true in my heart? Jesus is the Son of God who died to take away the sins of the world, my sins as well as yours, and He rose again from the dead."

The commander and Titus didn't know what to say. They simply sat quietly, thinking about the amazing story they had just heard—the story about Jesus of Nazareth, the Son of God who had come to earth to be the Savior of the world.

"And now that you have heard the story," John continued, "tell me, what will you believe?" †

Bibliography

Augsburger, Myron (1982). *The Communicator's Commentary Series, Volume 1: Matthew:* Waco: Word Books.

Culpepper, R. A. (1994). *John, the Son of Zebedee: the Life of a Legend.* Edinburgh, Scotland: T&T Clark Ltd.

Deuteronomy. (1966). *The Jerusalem Bible - Reader's Edition.* (A. Jones, Ed.) New York: Doubleday.

Farmer, W. R. (1998). *The International Bible Commentary.* Collegeville: The Order of St. Benedict.

Fredrickson, Roger L. (1985). *The Communicator's Commentary Series, Volume 4: John:* Waco: Word Books.

Geil, W. E. (1896). *The Isle That Is Called Patmos.* Philadelphia: American Baptist Publication Society.

McKenna, David (1982). *The Communicator's Commentary Series, Volume 2: Mark:* Waco: Word Books.

Mounce, R. H. (1998). *The Book of Revelation (The New International Commentary on the New Testament).* Grand Rapids: Wm. B. Eerdmans Publishing Company.

Study Questions

The Old Prisoner (page 1)

1. Where was the "old prisoner" taken?
2. Who sent the prisoner to jail?
3. Why was he put in prison?
4. Who did the prisoner believe Jesus was?

The Child (page 5)

1. What prophecy did God give so people would recognize His Son?
2. Who was chosen to be the mother of God's Son?
3. How did she receive the news that she had been chosen?
4. What name was she to give the child?
5. Why do you think people long ago found it hard to believe Jesus was God's Son? Why do they find it so hard today? Do you find it hard to believe that?

King Herod (page 7)

1. Where did King Herod live?
2. What mission did Herod send his soldiers on?
3. Why did King Herod send the soldiers on a mission?
4. How did Joseph know to take Mary and Jesus and escape?
5. To what country did they escape?

The Voice in the Wilderness (page 12)

1. In what town did Jesus' family finally settle?
2. How old was Jesus when He began His ministry?
3. Why did the Pharisees dislike the Baptist?
4. Why did Jesus want to be baptized?
5. What unusual thing happened when Jesus rose from the water?

The Temptation (page 17)

1. Why was Jesus in the desert?
2. How long was He there?
3. Whose voice spoke to Him in the desert?
4. How did Jesus answer the "voice"?

The Fishermen (page 19)

1. What were the names of the four fishermen?
2. What problem did the fishermen have?
3. What did Jesus tell them to do?
4. What happened when the men obeyed Jesus?
5. Sometimes it's not easy to do what we know God wants us to do but when we obey, things turn out better than expected. Has that ever happened to you?

The Call (page 24)

1. Who was Jesus calling?
2. What did He say to them?
3. What did He tell them they would be fishing for?
4. Does Jesus call all of us to share the Gospel or was it only a job for the apostles?

Healing (page 28)

1. Why did some men tear up Peter's roof?
2. What was wrong with the men's friend?
3. What two things did Jesus say to the man when He healed him?
4. Why were the Pharisees upset by Jesus' words?
5. Why can Jesus forgive sins? How does Jesus' forgiveness of our sins help us to forgive others?

The Pharisee Council (page 33)

1. Who were the Pharisees?
2. Why did they dislike Jesus?
3. What does the word *blasphemy* mean?
4. What was Jesus doing for people?

Twelve Men (page 37)

1. What did Jesus do to find strength for His work?
2. Why did Jesus send His disciples on a journey?
3. What did Jesus say would be their reward?
4. What did Jesus mean when He said, "If you lose your life for My sake, you will find it"?

Forgiven (page 41)

1. Why was the white-bearded Pharisee so upset in this story?
2. Why was the woman who had sinned brought before Jesus?
3. According to the Pharisees, what should happen to this woman?
4. What did Jesus do with the woman and the Pharisees?
5. What did the Pharisees do? What did Jesus tell the woman?

The Secret Believer (page 47)

1. Who was Nicodemus?
2. Why would Nicodemus wait until night to come and see Jesus?
3. What does it mean to be "born again"?
4. Why did God send Jesus into the world?

King of Israel (page 49)

1. What is a miracle?
2. Have you ever experienced a miracle? What happened?
3. How many people did Jesus feed? How much food did He have to feed them with?
4. What did Jesus tell His disciples would happen when they went to Jerusalem?
5. What new ideas did Jesus teach people who listened to Him?

Judas (page 53)

1. What did Judas promise to do for the Pharisees?
2. What did the Pharisees promise him in return?
3. Why do you think Judas made the decision to turn against Jesus?
4. How would you feel if someone you trusted turned against you?

Hosanna! (page 55)

1. What happened when Jesus entered Jerusalem?
2. What did the people put on the ground in front of Jesus?
3. What did the people cry out?
4. What did the disciples think about Jesus' welcome?
5. What did the Pharisees think about Jesus' welcome?

My Father's House (page 57)

1. What activity in the temple angered Jesus?
2. What did He do to those who angered Him?
3. What did Jesus say the temple was supposed to be used for?
4. What was Jesus talking about when He said, "Destroy this temple, and I will raise it up in three days"?

One Man Must Die (page 62)

1. Why were the Pharisees so angry with Jesus now?
2. What title did the people give Jesus?
3. Who was Caiaphas?
4. Who did the black-bearded Pharisee go see, to help him find Jesus?

The Last Supper (page 65)

1. What is a Passover festival?
2. Why did Jesus wash His disciples' feet?
3. Why did they think it was wrong for Him to do so?
4. What sign did Jesus give to point out the disciple who would betray Him?

Sorrow (page 69)

1. Where did Jesus and the disciples celebrate Passover?
2. Did the disciples understand what Jesus meant when He called the bread His body, and the wine His blood?
3. What did Jesus tell the disciples when they went out to the courtyard?
4. What did Peter do?
5. What did Jesus tell him?

The Arrest (page 72)

1. When Jesus went to the Garden of Gethsemane to pray, who did He take with Him?
2. How did Judas betray Jesus?
3. What did Peter do to protect Jesus? How did Jesus respond?
4. What would you have done if you had been in the garden with Jesus that night?

The High Priest (page 77)

1. Who was the high priest?

2. What did John see that caused his tears to flow?

3. Where was Peter?

4. How did Jesus answer the accusations against Him?

5. What judgment was Jesus given by the crowd?

6. Peter was afraid. Have you ever been afraid to say you are a Christian?

Judas' Remorse (page 84)

1. Why did the Pharisees want to send Jesus to the Roman governor for judgment?

2. Why did Judas return to the Pharisees after Jesus' arrest?

3. What did Judas do with the 30 pieces of silver?

4. What did Judas do when he felt so guilty?

5. Do you think Judas understood what would happen when he betrayed Jesus? Why or why not?

Suffering (page 86)

1. Who was Pontius Pilate?

2. Did Pilate think Jesus should be killed?

3. What "royal treatment" did the soldiers give Jesus?

4. What kind of crown did the soldiers put on Jesus' head?

Crucify Him! (page 90)

1. What was the name of the Roman governor who judged Jesus?

2. How was Jesus punished?

3. Who did the people want set free, instead of Jesus?

4. What did they want done to Jesus?

5. What symbol did Pilate use to show that he believed Jesus was innocent?

The Place of the Skull (page 94)

1. What was Jesus made to carry?
2. Who was behind Him?
3. What happened when Jesus reached Golgotha?
4. What did Jesus say as He hung on the cross?
5. What was written on the sign that hung above Jesus' head?
6. What were Jesus' last words?
7. What happened at the temple after Jesus died?

The Third Day (page 104)

1. Where was Jesus buried?
2. Why did the Pharisees go to Pilate after Jesus' burial?
3. What frightened the guards at Jesus' tomb?

He Is Alive! (page 108)

1. What did the disciples do after Jesus' death?
2. How were the disciples feeling?
3. How many days had it been since Jesus died?
4. Who knocked at the door where the disciples were staying?
5. What did she tell them?

My Lord and My God! (page 110)

1. Why is the disciple, Thomas, known as the doubter?
2. What convinced Thomas that the other disciples were telling the truth?
3. What did Peter and Jesus talk about on their walk?
4. What did Jesus mean when He told Peter, "Feed My sheep"?
5. What would you say to someone who doubts Jesus is the Son of God? How would you help someone believe?

A Witness Until the End (page 114)

1. Who was the "old prisoner"?
2. What did he say he was?
3. What did Jesus tell the disciples the last time they were all together?
4. Do you think the soldiers believed the "old prisoner"?
5. Do you believe?

Notes:

_____

_____

_____

_____

_____

_____

_____

_____

_____

_____

_____

_____

_____

_____

_____

_____

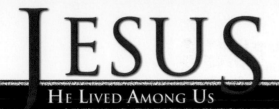

JESUS
HE LIVED AMONG US

Warner Press®

Warner Press is a not-for-profit organization that publishes and distributes Christian products to equip churches for ministry, as well as encourage individual spiritual growth. For more than 130 years, Warner Press has been sharing the gospel of Jesus Christ and serving the Christian community worldwide. For more information about Warner Press Christian products, check with your local Christian retailer or visit www.warnerpress.org.

Warner Press is honored to partner with The Voice of the Martyrs to publish this new illustrated storybook, *Jesus: He Lived Among Us*. Based on the biblical account of the life of Jesus, this book will serve as the companion piece to The Voice of the Martyrs animated film by the same title. For more information about the new film, please go to www.thejesusmovie.com.

VISION VIDEO

Don't miss the action-packed DVD that brings the stories in this book to life. Follow John's eyewitness account of the true story of the life of Jesus in this animated DVD available at most Christian retailers. For more information, please contact your local retailer or contact Vision Video at 1.800.523.0226 or www.visionvideo.com.

UPC:	7 27985 01417 3
Product Code:	501417D
Format:	DVD
Running Time:	90 minutes
Price:	$14.99 USD
Special Features:	English and Spanish language tracks
	Optional English and Spanish subtitles
	A visual presentation of The Voice of the Martyrs

The Voice of the Martyrs is a nonprofit, interdenominational Christian organization dedicated to assisting the persecuted church worldwide. VOM was founded in 1967 by Pastor Richard Wurmbrand, who was imprisoned 14 years in Communist Romania for his faith in Christ. His wife, Sabina, was imprisoned three years. In the 1960s, Richard, Sabina, and their son, Mihai, were ransomed out of Romania and came to the United States. Through their travels, the Wurmbrands spread the message of the atrocities that Christians face in restricted nations and established a network of offices dedicated to assisting the persecuted church. The Voice of the Martyrs continues in this mission around the world today.

Our ministry is based on Hebrews 13:3, "Remember them that are in bonds, as bound with them; and them which suffer adversity, as being yourselves also in the body," and is focused on the following main purposes:

HELP

VOM helps Christians who are or have been persecuted for their involvement in spreading the gospel of Jesus Christ. We provide medical assistance, food, clothing and other forms of aid.

LOVE

VOM supports Christians who are willing to invite their fellow men, even their persecutors, to Jesus Christ through faithful deeds of love in a hostile environment. We supply Bibles, literature, radios, and other evangelistic tools.

ENCOURAGE

VOM encourages persecuted Christians by giving their testimony a voice, informing Christians in the USA of how to help. We believe the lives and testimonies of persecuted Christians are vital parts of the fellowship of all believers and will challenge and strengthen the faith of Christians everywhere.

You can learn more, and sign up for VOM's free monthly newsletter by visiting www.persecution.com.

To learn more about the *Jesus: He Lived Among Us* video, visit www.thejesusmovie.com.